SCHOLASTIC

# Maths SATs Challenge Ages 10–11

Challenge

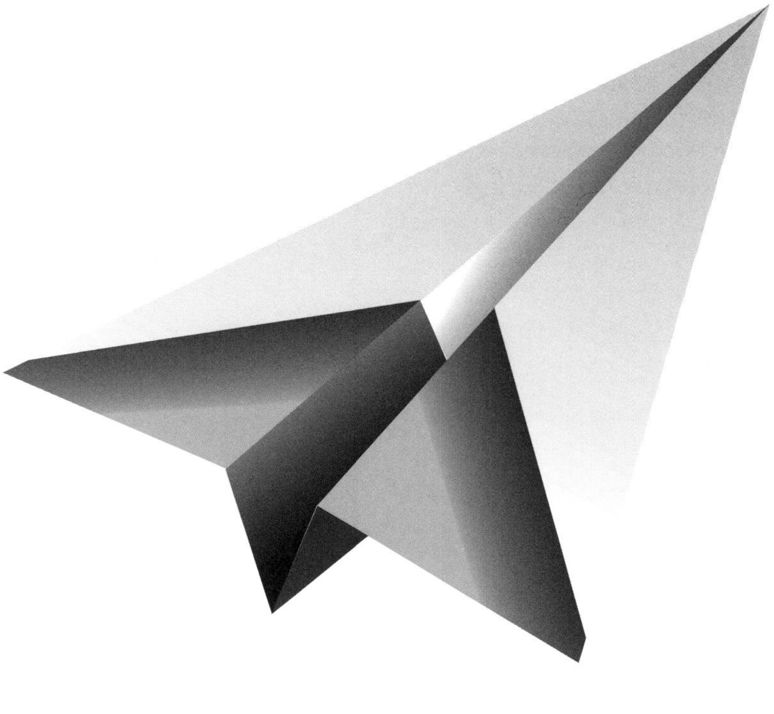

KS2
Year 6

Aim for greater depth in the Year 6 National Tests

Published in the UK by Scholastic, 2018
Scholastic Distribution Centre, Bosworth Avenue, Tournament Fields, Warwick, CV34 6UQ
Scholastic Ireland, 89E Lagan Road, Dublin Industrial Estate, Glasnevin, Dublin, D11 HP5F

www.scholastic.co.uk


2 3 4 5 6 7 8 9      3 4 5 6 7 8 9 0 1 2

A CIP catalogue record for this book is available from the British Library.
ISBN 978-1407-17545-4

Printed and bound by Ashford Colour Press Ltd, Gosport, Hampshire, PO13 0FW

Paper made from wood grown in sustainable forests and other controlled sources.



**Authors** Hilary Koll and Steve Mills

**Editorial** Rachel Morgan, Shannon Keenlyside, Audrey Stokes, Julia Roberts

**Series Design** Neil Salt and Nicolle Thomas

**Layout** Claire Green

**Illustration** page 38 illustration: Tom Heard/The Bright Agency

# Contents

# How to use this book

This *Workbook* helps you to check what you already know, practise what you've learned and challenge yourself to fly higher!

You can work through all of the activities in order or you can dip in and out to brush up your skills or explore in more depth. Use the progress chart opposite to record which skills you've checked and practised.

You can check the answers at the back of the book.

What you should be able to do after you complete the skills check and practice questions. You can tick off each one as you can do it.

The title of the topic.

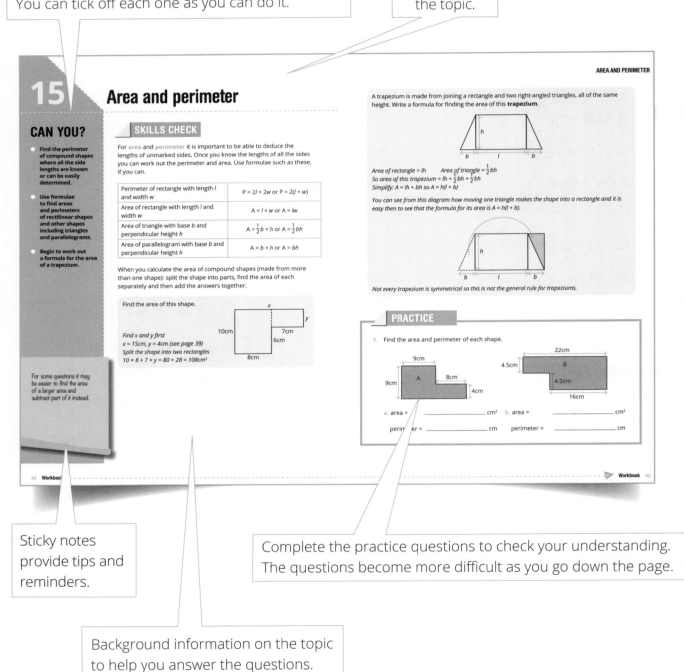

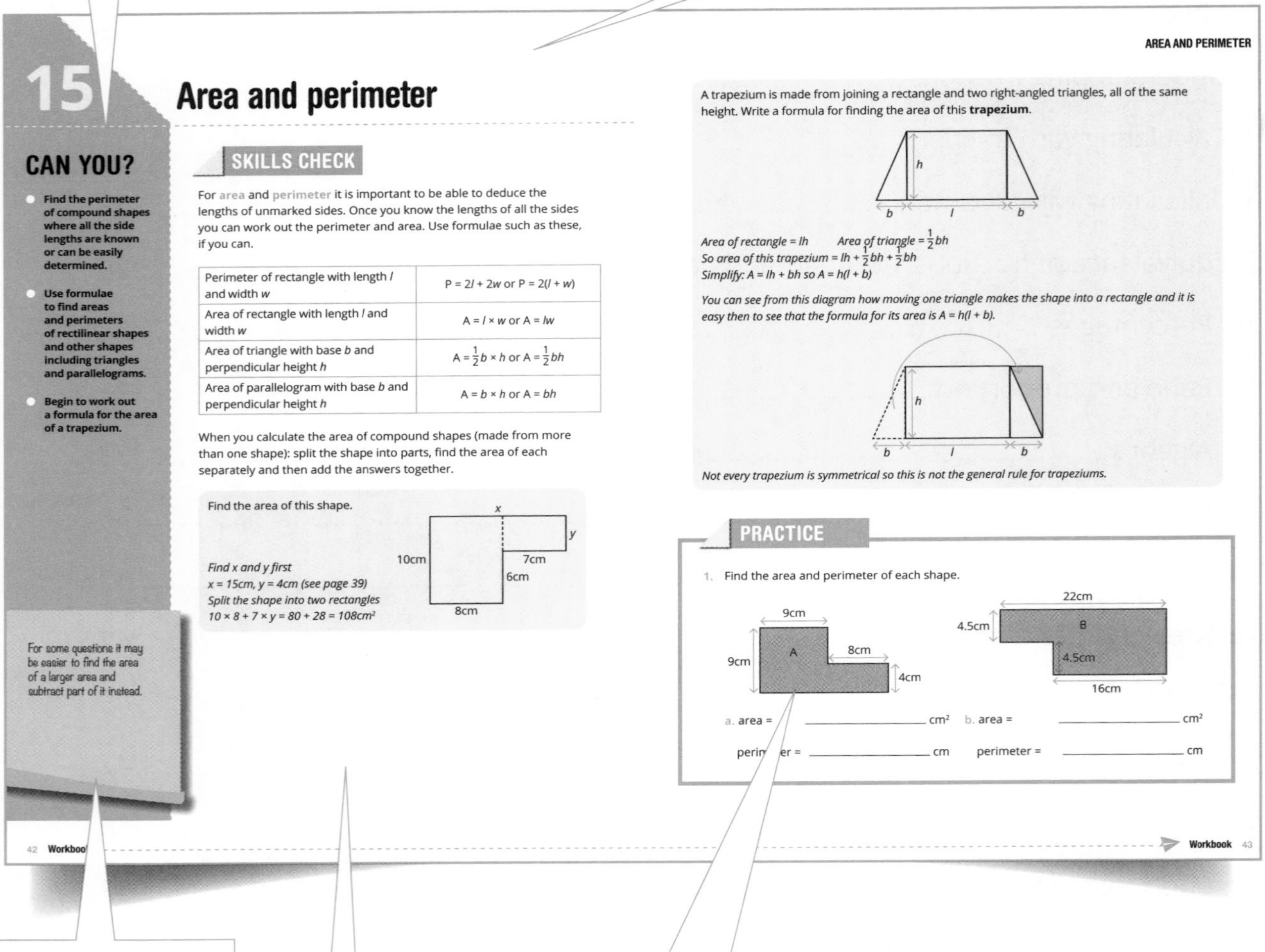

AREA AND PERIMETER

15

## Area and perimeter

**CAN YOU?**

- Find the perimeter of compound shapes where all the side lengths are known or can be easily determined.
- Use formulae to find areas and perimeters of rectilinear shapes and other shapes including triangles and parallelograms.
- Begin to work out a formula for the area of a trapezium.

For some questions it may be easier to find the area of a larger area and subtract part of it instead.

**SKILLS CHECK**

For area and perimeter it is important to be able to deduce the lengths of unmarked sides. Once you know the lengths of all the sides you can work out the perimeter and area. Use formulae such as these, if you can.

| | |
|---|---|
| Perimeter of rectangle with length $l$ and width $w$ | $P = 2l + 2w$ or $P = 2(l + w)$ |
| Area of rectangle with length $l$ and width $w$ | $A = l \times w$ or $A = lw$ |
| Area of triangle with base $b$ and perpendicular height $h$ | $A = \frac{1}{2}b \times h$ or $A = \frac{1}{2}bh$ |
| Area of parallelogram with base $b$ and perpendicular height $h$ | $A = b \times h$ or $A = bh$ |

When you calculate the area of compound shapes (made from more than one shape): split the shape into parts, find the area of each separately and then add the answers together.

Find the area of this shape.

*Find x and y first*
*x = 15cm, y = 4cm (see page 39)*
*Split the shape into two rectangles*
*$10 \times 8 + 7 \times y = 80 + 28 = 108cm^2$*

A trapezium is made from joining a rectangle and two right-angled triangles, all of the same height. Write a formula for finding the area of this **trapezium**.

*Area of rectangle = $lh$ Area of triangle = $\frac{1}{2}bh$*
*So area of this trapezium = $lh + \frac{1}{2}bh + \frac{1}{2}bh$*
*Simplify: $A = lh + bh$ so $A = h(l + b)$*

*You can see from this diagram how moving one triangle makes the shape into a rectangle and it is easy then to see that the formula for its area is $A = h(l + b)$.*

*Not every trapezium is symmetrical so this is not the general rule for trapeziums.*

**PRACTICE**

1. Find the area and perimeter of each shape.

a. area = ________ cm²
perimeter = ________ cm

b. area = ________ cm²
perimeter = ________ cm

42 Workbook
Workbook 43

Sticky notes provide tips and reminders.

Complete the practice questions to check your understanding. The questions become more difficult as you go down the page.

Background information on the topic to help you answer the questions.

# Progress chart

| Topic | Skills checked | Practised | Aimed higher |
| --- | --- | --- | --- |
| Place value and negative numbers | | | |
| Properties of number | | | |
| Mental calculation | | | |
| Addition and subtraction | | | |
| Multiplication and division | | | |
| Understanding fractions | | | |
| Calculating with fractions | | | |
| Calculating with decimals | | | |
| Equivalence of fractions, decimals and percentages | | | |
| Percentages | | | |
| Ratio and proportion | | | |
| Algebra | | | |
| Units of measurement | | | |
| Measurement problems | | | |
| Area and perimeter | | | |
| Volume | | | |
| Properties of shapes | | | |
| Angles | | | |
| Coordinate grids and transformations | | | |
| Statistics | | | |

# 1 Place value and negative numbers

## CAN YOU?

- Identify the place value of each digit in any number up to ten million.
- Round large numbers to any degree of accuracy.
- Use negative numbers and calculate intervals across zero.
- Solve number problems that involve all of the above.

## SKILLS CHECK

Digits of large numbers are grouped in threes, often with a comma separating the millions from the thousands and from the ones.

| 10,000,000 | 1,000,000 | 100,000 | 10,000 | 1000 | 100 | 10 | 1 |
|---|---|---|---|---|---|---|---|
| | 9 | 6 | 0 | 1 | 9 | 1 | 0 |

↑ nine million ↑ six hundred and one thousand ↑ nine hundred and ten

When rounding, look to the digit to the right of the one you are rounding to. If it is 5 or more, round up. If not, round down.

Negative numbers are on the other side of zero from positive numbers. When calculating across zero, remember to include it like any other number.

What is the **difference** between the values of the two **9** digits in 9,601,910?

*Write the values of both digits in full first. 9,000,000 and 900*

*Find the difference by subtracting or counting up from the smaller number.*
*9,000,000 – 900 = 8,999,100*

Round 9,601,910 to the nearest 1000, to the nearest 10,000 and to the nearest 1,000,000.

*...to nearest 1000: 9,601,**9**10* → rounds up to 9,602,000

*...to nearest 10,000: 9,60**1**,910* → rounds down to 9,600,000

*...to nearest 1,000,000: 9,**6**01,910* → rounds up to 10,000,000

Identify the value of the number on the line marked with a cross.

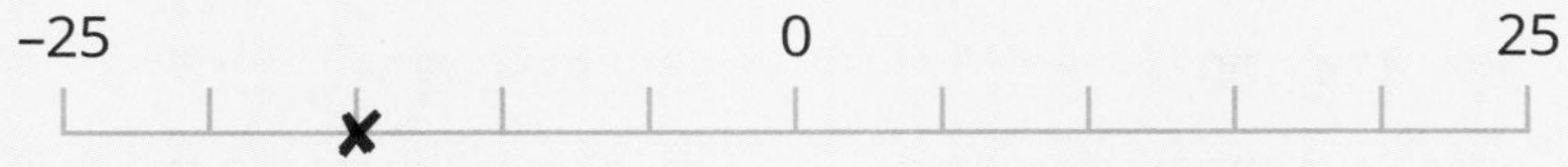


This number line has positive and negative numbers.

*There are 5 intervals between 0 and 25 so each must be worth 5.*
*Count back three 5s from zero.*
*The cross is at –15.*

## PRACTICE

1. Write each number in words.

a. 70,707 ____________________________________________

____________________________________________

b. 7,010,009 ____________________________________________

____________________________________________

2. Give the difference between the numbers in each pair.

a. –5 9 | b. 2000 5 | c. 60,000 600

3. Mark with a cross the number –10 on each of these number lines.

a.

b.

c.

d.

**4.** Find the difference between the values of the underlined digits in each number.

a. 3<u>7</u>3,55<u>7</u>

b. 1,<u>4</u>5<u>4</u>,500

c. <u>2</u>,050,0<u>2</u>0

[ ] [ ] [ ]

**5.** Add 50,000 to each number and round the answer to the nearest 10,000.

a. 168,000

b. 1,504,999

c. 7,095,000

[ ] [ ] [ ]

**6.** The sequences below increase or decrease in equal-sized steps.

Fill in the missing numbers.

a. [ ] [5] [11] [17] [ ]

b. [ ] [1] [21] [41] [ ]

c. [ ] [–17] [–9] [–1] [ ]

**7.** What are the lowest and highest whole numbers that, when rounded to the nearest 1000, give the answer 50,000?

lowest [ ] highest [ ]

2

# Properties of number

## CAN YOU?

**Find common factors and common multiples for two or more numbers.**

**Recall and use square numbers and cube numbers.**

**Recognise prime numbers and find and use prime factors.**

1 is not a prime number as it only has one factor.

## SKILLS CHECK

A **common factor** of two or more numbers is a number that divides into them all without a remainder. The common factors of 12 and 18 are 1, 2, 3 and 6. The **highest common factor** of 12 and 18 (the largest of the factors) is 6.

A **common multiple** of two or more numbers is a number into which all of the numbers divide without a remainder. The common multiples of 4 and 6 are 12, 24, 36 and every other multiple of 12. The **lowest common multiple** of 4 and 6 (the smallest of them) is 12.

A **square number** is a whole number multiplied by itself. $4^2 = 4 \times 4 = 16$

Examples of square numbers are: 1, 4, 9, 16, 25, 36, 49...

A **cube number** is a whole number multiplied by itself and then by itself again. $4^3 = 4 \times 4 \times 4 = 64$

Examples of cube numbers are: 1, 8, 27, 64, 125, 216...

A **prime number** only has two factors, itself and 1.

Examples of prime numbers are: 2, 3, 5, 7, 11, 13, 17, 19...

Write the number 70 as the product of its **prime factors**.

*(Make a multiplication where each number in the question is prime.)*

*70 =* ☐ × ☐ × ☐

*70 = 2 × 5 × 7*

Jo thinks of a **cube number** that lies between 250 and 600.

What two numbers could Jo be thinking of?

*6 × 6 × 6 = 216, 7 × 7 × 7 = 343, 8 × 8 × 8 = 512, 9 × 9 × 9 = 729*

The answers are 343 and 512 as only these two lie between 250 and 600.

Connor adds a cube number to a square number to equal a prime number.

Fill in possible numbers he could have used to make the statement true.

*cube* *square* *prime*

☐ + ☐ = ☐

*Try adding different cube and square numbers until you make a prime number, such as 8 + 9 = 17 or 27 + 4 = 31.*

## PRACTICE

1. Write these numbers into the correct sections of this diagram.

| 2 | 4 | 17 | 39 | 100 |
|---|---|---|---|---|

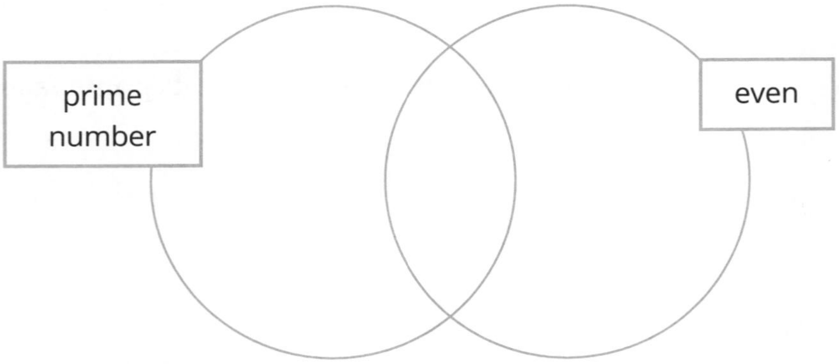


2. Fill each box with a prime, cube or square number as shown to make these additions correct.

*prime* *prime* *square*

☐ + ☐ = ☐

*square* *prime* *cube*

☐ + ☐ = ☐

3. Here is a diagram for sorting numbers.

| | Multiples of 8 | Not multiples of 8 |
|---|---|---|
| Multiples of 12 | | |
| Not multiples of 12 | | |

Complete this statement to make it true.

The lowest number that can be written into the shaded section of the diagram is ☐

4. Give the lowest common multiple of:

a. 14 and 8. ☐

b. 16 and 6. ☐

5. Write 54 and 90 as the product of their prime factors.

54 = ☐ × ☐ × ☐ × ☐

90 = ☐ × ☐ × ☐ × ☐

Use your answers to help you give the **highest common factor** of 54 and 90.

________________________________________

6. Give the highest common factor of:

a. 210 and 63. ☐

b. 270 and 45. ☐

# 3 Mental calculation

## CAN YOU?

- **Perform mental calculations, including with mixed operations and large numbers.**
- **Use knowledge of the order of operations to carry out calculations involving the four operations.**

## SKILLS CHECK

When working mentally with large multiples of powers of 10 it can help to think of them as small numbers and then adjust for the powers of 10. When multiplying and dividing, look very carefully at the sizes of the numbers in the question to make sure your answer has the correct number of zeros.

| | |
|---|---|
| *46,000 + 30,000 = 46 + 30 = 76* | *so the answer is 76,000* |
| *1,000,000 – 470,000 = 100 – 47 = 53* | *so the answer is 530,000* |
| *8000 × 900 = 8 × 9 = 72* | *so the answer is 7,200,000* |
| *420,000 ÷ 60 = 42 ÷ 6 = 7* | *so the answer is 7000* |

Use BIDMAS to remember the order in which you carry out calculations.

Brackets Indices Divide and Multiply Add and Subtract

First, do calculations in brackets. If you have more than one set of brackets, complete each set before moving on. Indices are powers such as $5^2 = 5 \times 5$ or $7^3 = 7 \times 7 \times 7$. Do these next. Finally, complete the rest in this order; Divide and Multiply (from left to right), then Add and Subtract (from left to right).

$30 - 5^2 + 3 \times (1 + 4)$

| | |
|---|---|
| Brackets first: | $30 - 5^2 + 3 \times 5$ |
| Indices: | $30 - 25 + 3 \times 5$ |
| Division and multiplication: | $30 - 25 + 15$ |
| Addition and subtraction from left to right: | 20 |

## PRACTICE

1. Answer each question using mental methods.

a. 550,000 + 90,000 =

b. 175,000 + 25,000 =

c. 70,000 – 25,000 =

d. 820,000 – 40,000 =

e. 70 × 800 =

f. 40,000 × 60 =

g. 640,000 ÷ 8 =

h. 49,000,000 ÷ 70 =

2. Write the missing numbers to make the multiplication grids correct.

| × | | |
|---|---|---|
| 40 | 2800 | 3600 |
| | 4900 | 6300 |

| × | | |
|---|---|---|
| 90 | 540 | 1080 |
| | 720 | 1440 |

3. Give the value of each expression.

a. $8 - 6 \div 2 + 6 \times 5$

b. $10 \times 3^2 + (8 - 6) \div 2$

c. $7 + 4^2 - 10 \div (5 + 5)$

d. $2^3 + 3^2 \times (4 - 1)$

4. Circle the expression that is greater and write by how much it is greater.

a. $4^2 - 3 \times (5 - 5) + 7$ $\quad$ $4^2 - (3 \times 5) - 5 + 7$

b. $9 \div (2 + 1) \times 2^2$ $\quad$ $9 \div 2 + (1 \times 2^2)$

c. $(6^2 + 8^2) \times 3^2 - 9$ $\quad$ $6^2 + 8^2 \times (3^2 - 9)$

# 4 Addition and subtraction

## CAN YOU?

- Solve addition and subtraction multi-step problems involving increasingly large numbers in contexts.
- Use estimation to check answers to calculations involving increasingly large numbers.

## SKILLS CHECK

When solving problems involving several steps, marks are often given for showing your methods. Show clearly whether you plan to add, subtract, multiply or divide for each calculation.

If using a written method of addition or subtraction, set out the numbers carefully in columns and show all the carrying marks. Write your final answer clearly in the answer box.

How much greater is 1,105,008 than the **sum** of 26,364 and 887,945?

| | | | | | | |
|---|---|---|---|---|---|---|
| | 8 | 8 | 7 | 9 | 4 | 5 |
| + | | 2 | 6 | 3 | 6 | 4 |
| | 9 | 1 | 4 | 3 | 0 | 9 |
| | 1 | 1 | 1 | 1 | | |

| | | | | | | | |
|---|---|---|---|---|---|---|---|
| | | 10 | 1 | 4 | 9 | 9 | 1 |
| | ~~1~~ | ~~1~~ | 0 | ~~5~~ | ~~0~~ | ~~0~~ | 8 |
| − | | 9 | 1 | 4 | 3 | 0 | 9 |
| | | 1 | 9 | 0 | 6 | 9 | 9 |

190,699

Use inverse calculations and estimation to check your answers.

***Using estimation:*** *887,945 is about 890,000, 26,364 is about 30,000 so the total should be about 920,000.*

*1,105,008 is about 1,110,000. That is about 190,000 more than 920,000, so the answer 190,699 seems about right.*

***Using inverses:*** *To check the addition, take 26,364 from your answer 914,309 to see if you get 887,945.*

*To check the subtraction, add 914,309 to your answer 190,699 to see if you get 1,105,008.*

*When solving missing digit problems you can also use inverse calculations to work out the missing digits. Start with the 1s column and work to the left.*

For additions, use subtraction to check your answers and for subtractions, use addition to check.

## PRACTICE

1. Write four missing digits to make each calculation correct.

a.

| | | | | |
|---|---|---|---|---|
| | | 1 | | 1 |
| − | 2 | | 3 | |
| | 4 | 5 | 0 | 7 |

b.

| | | | | |
|---|---|---|---|---|
| | | 0 | | 5 |
| − | 7 | | 2 | |
| | 1 | 8 | 9 | 6 |

c.

| | | | | |
|---|---|---|---|---|
| | | 3 | | 9 |
| + | 1 | | 9 | |
| | 4 | 0 | 0 | 8 |

2. There are 42,157 seats in a stadium. There are 7937 empty seats. Of the people sitting in the other seats, 15,286 are children. How many adults are sitting in the stadium?

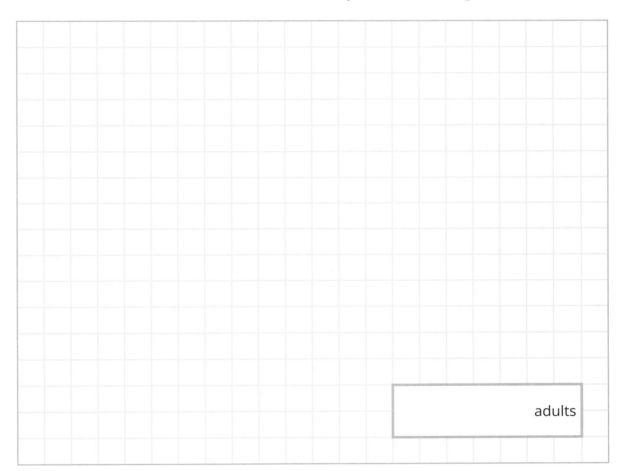

adults

3. Use estimation to help you find the answer to the question 376,485 + 582,375 – 437,636. Circle the answer:

1,396,496 743,224 74,224 696,496 521,224

# 5 Multiplication and division

## CAN YOU?

- **Solve problems involving multiplication and division.**
- **Multiply numbers up to four digits by 2- and 3-digit whole numbers, using the formal written method of long multiplication.**
- **Divide numbers up to four digits by a 2-digit whole number using the formal written method of long division and short division.**
- **Can interpret remainder as whole number remainders, fractions or by rounding, as appropriate for the context.**

## SKILLS CHECK

In the arithmetic paper, questions are included that test long multiplication and long and short division. Set out your calculations correctly and show all your working, writing your final answer in the answer box.

**Long multiplication**

7283 × 75

| | | | | | | |
|---|---|---|---|---|---|---|
| | | 7 | 2 | 8 | 3 | |
| × | | | | 7 | 5 | |
| | 3 | $6_1$ | $4_4$ | $1_1$ | 5 | 7283×5 |
| 5 | $0_1$ | $9_5$ | $8_2$ | 1 | 0 | 7283×70 |
| 5 | 4 | 6 | 2 | 2 | 5 | |
| | 1 | 1 | | | | |

**Short division**

8736 ÷ 6

| | | | | |
|---|---|---|---|---|
| | 1 | 4 | 5 | 6 |
| 6 | 8 | $^2$7 | $^3$3 | $^3$6 |

**Long division**

7344 ÷ 16

| | | | | | | |
|---|---|---|---|---|---|---|
| | | | | 4 | 5 | 9 |
| 1 | 6 | 7 | 3 | 4 | 4 | |
| | – | 6 | 4 | | | |
| | | | 9 | 4 | | |
| | | – | 8 | 0 | | |
| | | | 1 | 4 | 4 | |
| | | – | 1 | 4 | 4 | |
| | | | | | 0 | |

For division problems think carefully about whether to give an answer with a remainder as a mixed number or decimal, in pence or even rounded to the nearest whole number.

A problem that requires the division 416 ÷ 11 might have any of these answers:

37 r 9 $37\frac{9}{5}$ 37.81818... 37 £37.82 38

| | | | | | | |
|---|---|---|---|---|---|---|
| | | | 3 | 7 | r | 9 |
| 1 | 1 | 4 | 1 | 6 | | |
| | – | 3 | 3 | ↓ | | |
| | | | 8 | 6 | | |
| | | – | 7 | 7 | | |
| | | | | 9 | | |

How many packs of 11 biscuits should Amira buy if she wants to give one biscuit to each of the 416 people in a care home?
*Here we must round the answer up.*
*Amira must buy 38 packs to have enough biscuits.*

How many £11 T-shirts can be bought with £416?
*Here we must round the answer down.*
*Only 37 T-shirts can be bought.*

Work from right to left for long multiplication and from left to right for long and short division.

## PRACTICE

1. How much greater is the answer to 2735 × 724 than the answer to 273 × 5724?

2. Answer this question using short division and then using long division. 756 ÷ 12

3. Solve these problems.

a. Kai earns on average £47 each day in January.
How much will he earn in the whole month?

£

b. There are 28 days in February. Kai earns £1323 in February.
How much is this on average each day?

£

c. How many £79 flights can be bought with £495?

d. How many packs of 16 biscuits must Petya buy to have 758 biscuits?

4. £1370 is shared equally between 6 people. How much will each person get?
Circle the best answer to this problem.

228 £228 r 2 £228 £228 £228.333333 £228.33 £229

6

# Understanding fractions

## CAN YOU?

- Use common multiples to express fractions in the same denomination.
- Compare and order fractions, including fractions greater than 1.
- Use common factors to simplify fractions.
- Solve problems involving fractions.

## SKILLS CHECK

It is often easier to work with fractions when they all have the same denominator. Change fractions to equivalent ones with a common denominator by multiplying or dividing both numbers of each fraction by the same number.

Give a fraction that lies between these two fractions:

$\frac{3}{5}$ and $\frac{5}{8}$

*First change both fractions to have the denominator that is the **lowest common multiple** of 5 and 8, which is 40.*

$\frac{3}{5} = \frac{24}{40}$ $\quad \frac{5}{8} = \frac{25}{40}$

*Sometimes it is then easy to give a fraction that lies between them, but here change both new fractions to have the denominator 80.*

$\frac{24}{40} = \frac{48}{80}$ $\quad \frac{25}{40} = \frac{50}{80}$

*So a fraction that lies between them could be* $\frac{49}{80}$

Writing a fraction in its simplest form is useful when comparing fractions. Divide both numbers of a fraction by a common factor to simplify it. Also convert mixed numbers to improper fractions or vice versa, to make them the same.

Circle the fraction that is equivalent to $\frac{16}{20}$.

$\frac{3}{5}$ $\quad \frac{40}{100}$ $\quad \frac{4}{10}$ $\quad \frac{12}{15}$ $\quad \frac{3}{4}$

*Simplify* $\frac{16}{20}$ *to give* $\frac{4}{5}$ *and simplify the other fractions to see which is also equivalent to* $\frac{4}{5}$.

$\frac{3}{5}$ $\quad \frac{40}{100} = \frac{2}{5}$ $\quad \frac{4}{10} = \frac{2}{5}$ $\quad \frac{12}{15} = \frac{4}{5}$ (circled) $\quad \frac{3}{4}$

Tick which is greater: $\frac{15}{6}$ or $2\frac{2}{3}$

*Make both mixed numbers with denominator 6:*

$\frac{15}{6} = 2\frac{3}{6}$ *and* $2\frac{2}{3} = 2\frac{4}{6}$ *so* $2\frac{2}{3}$ *is greater.*

## PRACTICE

1. Tick the fraction which is greater in each pair.

a. $\frac{2}{5}$ ☐ or $\frac{3}{8}$ ☐ b. $\frac{5}{6}$ ☐ or $\frac{7}{8}$ ☐ c. $\frac{5}{3}$ ☐ or $1\frac{5}{8}$ ☐

d. $2\frac{7}{10}$ ☐ or $2\frac{5}{8}$ ☐ e. $\frac{3}{4}$ ☐ or $\frac{8}{11}$ ☐ f. $\frac{23}{5}$ ☐ or $4\frac{3}{4}$ ☐

2. Give a fraction that lies between the two fractions in each pair.

a. $\frac{4}{7}$ and $\frac{3}{4}$ b. $\frac{3}{5}$ and $\frac{5}{10}$ c. $\frac{5}{8}$ and $\frac{2}{3}$

3. Put these fractions in order, starting with the smallest.

$\frac{5}{8}$ $\frac{5}{6}$ $\frac{7}{12}$ $\frac{2}{3}$ $\frac{13}{24}$

smallest ☐ ☐ ☐ ☐ ☐ largest

Explain how you can be sure that the fraction $\frac{2}{3}$ lies between the fractions $\frac{4}{7}$ and $\frac{5}{6}$.

___

___

7

# Calculating with fractions

## CAN YOU?

- **Add and subtract fractions with different denominators and mixed numbers, using the concept of equivalent fractions.**
- **Multiply pairs of proper fractions writing the answer in its simplest form.**
- **Divide proper fractions by whole numbers.**

Remember to simplify answers if you can.

## SKILLS CHECK

To add and subtract fractions make sure they all have the same denominator first and then add or subtract the numerator. To subtract mixed numbers, it can help to change them to improper fractions first.

$$\frac{3}{5} + \frac{5}{8} = \frac{24 + 25}{40} = \frac{49}{40} = 1\frac{9}{40}$$

$$3\frac{1}{4} - 1\frac{5}{6} = \frac{13}{4} - \frac{11}{6} = \frac{39 - 22}{12} = \frac{17}{12} = 1\frac{5}{12}$$

To multiply fractions it helps to simplify the question first. If you can, divide a numerator and a denominator by a common factor. Then multiply the numerators together, and then multiply the denominators together. Simplify the answer. Notice that, if the two fractions are less than 1, the answer is smaller than both of the original fractions.

$$\frac{\overset{1}{\cancel{5}}}{8} \times \frac{12}{\underset{3}{\cancel{15}}} = \frac{1}{\underset{2}{\cancel{8}}} \times \frac{\overset{3}{\cancel{12}}}{3} = \frac{1}{2} \times \frac{\overset{1}{\cancel{3}}}{\underset{1}{\cancel{3}}} = \frac{1}{2}$$

or $\frac{5}{8} \times \frac{12}{15} = \frac{60}{120} = \frac{1}{2}$

Some problems require multiplying a fraction by a whole number. You can write the whole number over 1 and simplify the question first in the same way.

What is $\frac{5}{6}$ of £366? $\quad \frac{5}{\underset{1}{\cancel{6}}} \times \frac{\overset{61}{\cancel{366}}}{1} = 5 \times 61 = 305 \quad$ *£305*

To divide a fraction by a whole number, write the question as an equivalent multiplication. Remember that dividing by 3 is like multiplying by $\frac{1}{3}$, dividing by 7 is like multiplying by $\frac{1}{7}$ and so on.

$\frac{4}{5} \div 3$ **is equivalent to** $\frac{4}{5} \times \frac{1}{3} = \frac{4}{15}$

## PRACTICE

1. Answer these calculations. Simplify your answers.

a. $\frac{7}{8} - \frac{5}{6}$

b. $3\frac{2}{3} + 2\frac{3}{8}$

c. $\frac{27}{36} \times \frac{15}{18}$

2. Find the product of one eighth and one sixth.

3. In a stadium $\frac{3}{8}$ of the 8480 people are children.
How many are children?

children

4. Explain how you can be sure that $\frac{3}{8} \div 6$ is equal to $\frac{1}{16}$

5. This sequence increases or decreases in equal-sized steps.
Fill in the missing numbers.

| | $1\frac{5}{9}$ | $2\frac{8}{9}$ | $4\frac{2}{9}$ | |
|---|---|---|---|---|

6. Write each answer in its simplest form.

a. $\frac{3}{12} \div 9 =$

b. $\frac{5}{9} \div 10 =$

# 8 Calculating with decimals

## CAN YOU?

- Identify the place value of each digit in any decimal number to three decimal places.
- Multiply and divide numbers by 10, 100 and 1000 giving answers up to three decimal places.
- Multiply 1-digit numbers with up to two decimal places by whole numbers.
- Solve problems involving decimals to three decimal places.
- Add and subtract decimals with different numbers of decimal places.

## SKILLS CHECK

Be sure to know the values of the digits in each column to the right of the decimal point, ie tenths (0.1), hundredths (0.01) and thousandths (0.001). When multiplying and dividing a number by 10, 100 and 1000, the digits of the number change columns.

5.5 ÷ 100
The digits 5 and 5 move two places to the right.

| 10s | 1s • | 0.1s | 0.01s | 0.001s |
|---|---|---|---|---|
| 0 | 0 • | 0 | 5 | 5 |

0.013 × 1000
The digits 1 and 3 move three places to the left.

| 10s | 1s • | 0.1s | 0.01s | 0.001s |
|---|---|---|---|---|
| 1 | 3 • | 0 | 0 | 0 |

For multiplication questions with 1-digit decimals rewrite them to include ÷10, ÷100, ÷1000.

$0.3 \times 7 = 3 \div 10 \times 7 = 3 \times 7 \div 10 = 21 \div 10 = 2.1$

$0.06 \times 4 = 6 \div 100 \times 4 = 6 \times 4 \div 100 = 24 \div 100 = 0.24$

$0.7 \times 900 = 7 \div 10 \times 9 \times 100 = 7 \times 9 \div 10 \times 100 = 63 \times 10 = 630$

To add and subtract decimals using a written method, line up the digits in the correct columns. It can help to write zeros in any empty columns. Use the normal method to add or subtract, remembering to write the decimal point in your answer.

8.7 – 2.674

| 10s | 1s • | 0.1s | 0.01s | 0.001s |
|---|---|---|---|---|
| | 8 • | ~~7~~ 6 | ~~10~~ 9 | 10 |
| | – 2 • | 6 | 7 | 4 |
| | 6 • | 0 | 2 | 6 |

When solving 'I think of a number' word puzzles, work backwards from the answer, using inverse operations.

I think of a number. I add 0.4 to it.
I divide the answer by 6, and get the result 0.4.
What was my number?

*Work backwards.*
*The inverse of ÷ 6 is × 6*
*0.4 × 6 = 2.4*

*The inverse of + 0.4 is – 0.4*
*2.4 – 0.4 = 2*
*My number is 2.*

Always line up the decimal point when adding and subtracting decimals.

## PRACTICE

1. a. 0.86 × 100 = ______

   b. 56 ÷ 1000 = ______

   c. 0.05 × 1000 = ______

   d. 650 ÷ 10 = ______

   e. 367.7 ÷ 100 = ______

   f. 0.809 × 100 = ______

2. a. 0.8 × 3 = ______

   b. 0.02 × 7 = ______

   c. 0.09 × 300 = ______

3. a. 7.7 – 1.083 =

b. 72.5 – 7.609 =

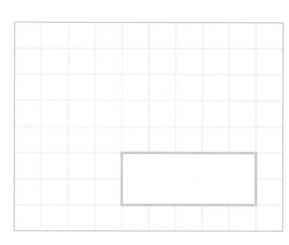

4. Yin chooses a decimal less than 1. She adds 0.8 to it and then divides this result by 2. Her answer is 0.7.

What was the decimal she started with?

5. Sayid chooses a number less than 20. He divides it by 5 and then adds 0.2. He then divides this result by 2. His answer is 1.5.

What was the number he started with?

6. Find the difference between the sum of 7.36 and 2.645 and the sum of 9.05 and 0.949.

7. Circle **two** numbers that add together to make 0.805.

0.005 0.3 0.55 0.8 0.05

9

# Equivalence of fractions, decimals and percentages

## CAN YOU?

- **Recall and use equivalences between simple fractions, decimals and percentages, including different contexts such as measures.**
- **Solve problems involving fractions, decimals and percentages.**

It can be helpful to memorise some of the most common fraction, decimal and percentage equivalents, eg

$\frac{1}{5} = 0.2 = 20\%$

## SKILLS CHECK

There are lots of different ways to convert between fractions, decimals and percentages. If a fraction can be written as an equivalent one with the denominator 10 or 100, do this first. Next, write the equivalent fraction as a decimal or percentage.

If the fraction cannot easily be written as an equivalent one with the denominator 10 or 100, then divide the numerator by the denominator using a written method of division.

Change $\frac{1}{5}$ and $\frac{7}{8}$ to percentages and decimals.

$\frac{1}{5} = \frac{2}{10}$ $\frac{20}{100}$ or 20% = 0.2 $\frac{7}{8} = ?$

*Since 8 is not a factor of 10 or 100, $\frac{7}{8}$ cannot be easily converted, so divide 7 by 8 like this:*

| | | | | | |
|---|---|---|---|---|---|
| | 0 | . | 8 | 7 | 5 |
| 8 | 7 | . | $^{7}0$ | $^{6}0$ | $^{4}0$ |

*So $\frac{7}{8} = 0.875 = 87.5\%$*

When solving problems involving fractions, decimals and percentages or comparing them, convert all the proportions to the same form and read carefully what form to give the answer in.

A bottle holds 0.7 litres of water. How much more does it hold than a bottle that has $\frac{13}{20}$ of a litre of water? Give your answer as a percentage of a litre.

$\frac{13}{20} = \frac{65}{100} = 0.65$

*The difference between 0.7 and 0.65 is 0.05.*
*0.05 as a percentage is 5%.*

## PRACTICE

1. Change each fraction to a percentage and a decimal.

   a. $\frac{17}{20}$ [ %] [ ]   b. $\frac{4}{5}$ [ %] [ ]

2. Change each decimal to a percentage and to a fraction (in its simplest form).

   a. 0.4 [ %] $\frac{\square}{\square}$   b. 0.375 [ %] $\frac{\square}{\square}$

3. Write $\frac{7}{11}$ as a decimal rounded to 3 decimal places.

4. Circle which is greater in each pair.

   a. 0.7 or 65%   b. 0.04 or 3.5%   c. 60% or $\frac{5}{8}$

5. A pot of paint contains 3.5 litres of paint. Tam uses $\frac{4}{5}$ of a litre of the paint on Monday and 1.8 litres on Tuesday.

   How much paint is left? [ litre]

   What is this answer as a percentage of a litre? [ %]

6. Six minutes is equal to one tenth of an hour.

   What percentage of an hour is 42 minutes? [ %]

# 10 Percentages

## CAN YOU?

- Solve problems involving the calculation of percentages and the use of percentages for comparison.

Percentage questions can be written using the word 'of' or using the multiplication sign, eg 45% of 900 or 45% x 900.

## SKILLS CHECK

Remember that any whole number percentage can be written as a fraction with the denominator 100. Use this idea to help write simple fractions as a percentage. Write the part of the whole on top of the fraction (the numerator) and the whole on the bottom of the fraction (the denominator) and convert to an equivalent fraction with the denominator 100.

$65\% = \frac{65}{100} = \frac{13}{20}$  $3\% = \frac{3}{100}$  $20\% = \frac{20}{100} = \frac{2}{10} = \frac{1}{5}$

I scored 23 out of 25 in a test. What percentage is this?

$\frac{23}{25} = \frac{?}{100}$ *Multiply the numerator and denominator by 4 to get* $\frac{92}{100}$ *which is 92%.*

160 out of 500 people in a crowd are adults. What percentage is this?

$\frac{160}{500} = \frac{?}{100}$ *Divide the numerator and denominator by 5 to get* $\frac{32}{100}$ *which is 32%.*

There are different methods to calculate a percentage of a quantity, such as using fractions, decimals or mental methods. Think carefully about the unit of your answer.

How long is a line that is 90% of the length of a 6cm line?

*Use a fraction:* $\frac{90}{100} \times 6 = \frac{9}{10} \times 6 = 5.4$

*Use a decimal:* $0.9 \times 6 = 5.4$

*Use mental methods:* *10% of 6 is 0.6*
*90% is 100% – 10%*
*so 6 – 0.6 = 5.4*

*The answer is either 5.4cm or 54mm.*

What is 61% × £600?

| | |
|---|---|
| *Use a fraction* | $\frac{61}{100} \times 600 = \frac{61}{1} \times 6 = 366$ |
| *Use a decimal* | *0.61 × 600 = 61 × 6 = 366* |
| *Use mental methods* | *50% of 600 is 300*<br>*10% of 600 is 60*<br>*1% of 600 is 6*<br>*300 + 60 + 6 = 366* |

The answer is £366.

## PRACTICE

1. Write the percentage of each grid that is shaded.

a. 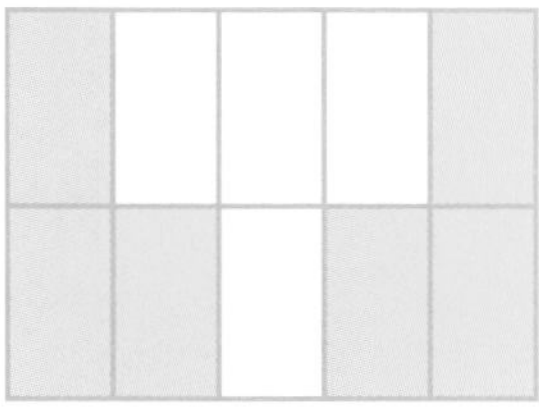

%

b. 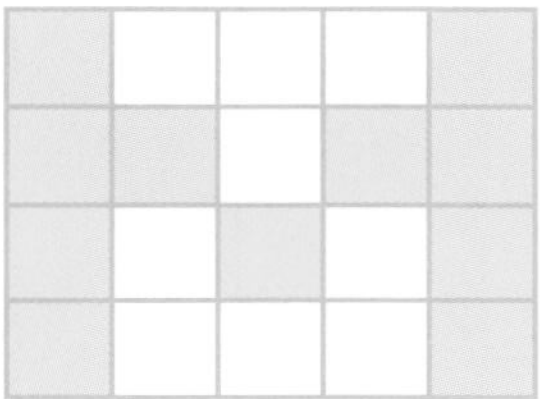

%

c. 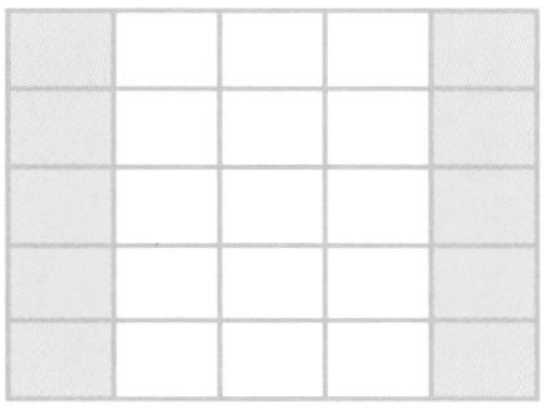

%

2. Write each proportion as a percentage.

a. 7 out of 10 = %

b. 13 out of 20 = %

c. 19 out of 25 = %

d. 450 out of 500 = %

e. 276 out of 300 = %

f. 184 out of 200 = %

3. a. 20% of 600 =

b. 15% × 700 =

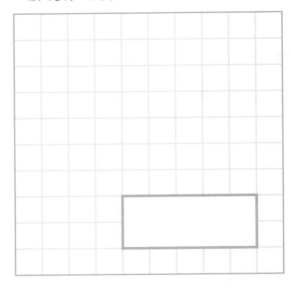

c. 85% of 120 =

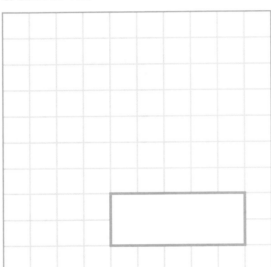

d. 3% × 280 =

4. A shop has a 40% sale. You pay 40% of the original price. How much would a football with an original price of £19 cost in the sale?

£

5. A shop has a 15% discount sale. 15% is taken off the original price. How much would a tennis racquet with an original price of £39 cost in the sale?

£

6. How many millimetres long is a line that is 30% of the length of an 8cm line?

mm

11

# Ratio and proportion

## CAN YOU?

- Solve problems involving the relative sizes of two quantities where missing values can be found by using integer multiplication and division facts.
- Use the notation *a:b* to record your work.
- Solve problems involving unequal sharing and grouping using knowledge of fractions and multiples.

## SKILLS CHECK

When solving ratio and proportion problems it can help to write the numbers using the notation ***a:b***.

To divide a whole into unequal parts write the total number of parts in the ratio, *a+b*.

For every 3 matches Tara wins, she loses 4 matches. Of the 28 matches, she has played, how many does she win?

| win | : | lose | total |
|---|---|---|---|
| 3 | : | 4 | 7 |
| ? | : | ? | 28 |

*Notice that 28 is 4 times greater than 7 so multiply 3 and 4 by 4 to give the answers 12 wins and 16 losses. Always check that they add to make the total. 12 + 16 = 28 ✓*

Remember that when two shapes are similar, one is an enlargement of the other with sides in the same ratio. This means that all the sides of the larger shape can be made by multiplying the sides of the smaller shape by the same number, the scale factor.

Two similar triangles are drawn. The first triangle has sides of 3cm, 4cm and 5cm. The second triangle has sides of 27cm, *y*cm and 45cm. What is the value of *y*?

*Write the lengths as ratios.*

$3 : 4 : 5$
$27 : y : 45$

*Notice that the numbers have been multiplied by the scale factor 9, so* $y = 4 \times 9 = 36$*cm.*

## PRACTICE

1. For every 5 cups of coffee Jake buys he gets 2 more free. How many free cups of coffee would he get for buying 20 cups of coffee?

2. A builder is making concrete. For every 2 parts of cement he uses he needs 3 parts of sand. He uses 18kg of sand. How much cement does he use?

   kg

3. For every 2 parts of cement the builder uses, he needs 3 parts of sand to make concrete. He wants to make 635kg of concrete altogether. How much cement and sand does he need?

   cement = kg   sand = kg

4. Circle which of these ratios is equivalent to 4:5.

   10:9   8:9   20: 25   16:10   12:20

5. The triangles in each pair are similar. Write the ratio of side *a* to side *b* for each pair.

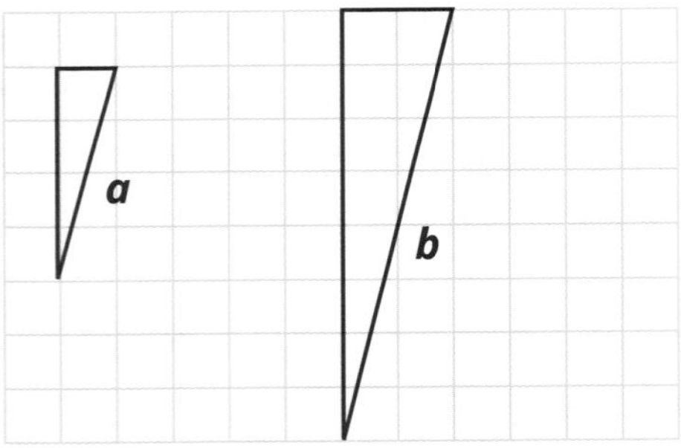


*a*:*b* =

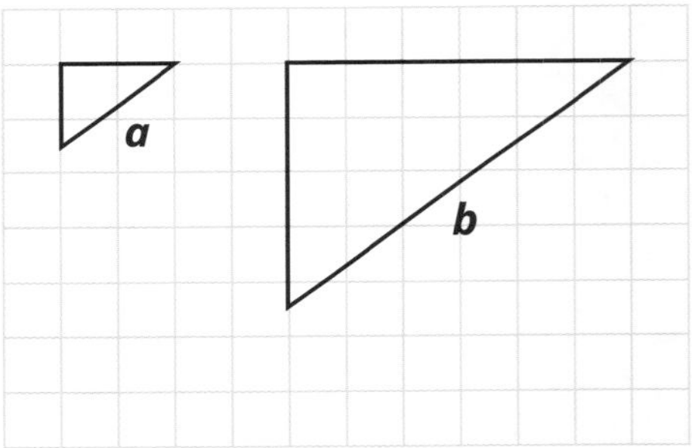


*a*:*b* =

6. Two similar rectangles are drawn. The first rectangle has sides of 4cm and 6.5cm. The second rectangle has sides of 28cm and *y* cm. What is the value of *y*?

   *y* = cm

# 12 Algebra

## CAN YOU?

- Solve simple equations that have unknown terms.
- Use simple formulae and begin to write simple formulae in words to describe situations.
- Generate, describe and complete linear number sequences, including those with missing terms.
- Express missing number problems algebraically for different contexts.

## SKILLS CHECK

To write situations as a **formula**, make sure you are clear about what each of the letters stands for. It can help to write them out.

A taxi-driver charges a basic fee of £4, plus £3 for each mile driven. Write a formula to show the cost ($C$) in pounds for a journey of $n$ miles.

*C is the total cost in pounds.*
*n is the number of miles driven.*

*$C = 4 + 3 \times n$*
*this can be written more simply as $C = 4 + 3n$*

Watch out for questions where the units are not the same, for example where prices are given in both pounds and in pence. Make sure you change them to both be the same.

A shop sells telephone cable by the metre. They charge £5 per order plus 40p per metre of cable ordered. Write the formula to show the cost ($C$) for $n$ metres of cable.

*C is the total cost (choose whether to be in pounds or in pence), n is the number of metres bought.*

*Change to pounds 40p = £0.40*

*$C$ (in pounds) $= 5 + 0.4 \times n$*
*this can be written more simply as $C = 5 + 0.4n$*

When substituting values into equations or formulae replace the letter with the given number.

Using the example above, find the cost for an order of 12 metres.

*For 12 metres, substitute 12 for n and find the cost.*

| | |
|---|---|
| | $C = 5 + 0.4 \times 12$ |
| *Multiply first!* | $5 + 4.8 = 9.8$ |

*Remember to express this in the correct unit.* $C = £9.80$

*Find the value of p when q is 4 in this equation.*

| | |
|---|---|
| | $7 - 3q^2 = p$ |
| | $7 - 3 \times 4^2 =$ |
| *Indices first,* | $7 - 3 \times 16 = p$ |
| *Then multiply,* | $7 - 48 = p$ |
| *Finally subtract,* | $7 - 48 = -41 \quad p = -41$ |

Remember to use
**B**rackets
**I**ndices
**D**ivision
**M**ultiplication
**A**ddition
**S**ubtraction

## PRACTICE

1. A taxi-driver charges a basic fee of £3, plus £1.50 for each mile driven. Write a formula to show the cost ($C$) in pounds for a journey of $n$ miles.

$C =$ ______________________

2. A shop sells telephone cable by the metre. They charge £3 per order plus 60p per metre of cable ordered. Write the formula to show the cost ($C$) in pounds for $n$ metres of cable. Then find the cost for an order of 9 metres of the cable.

$C$ = ______________________ Cost for 9m = ______________________

3. For each equation, find the value of $p$ when $q$ is 3.

a. $p = 5 + 2q$ $p$ = [ ]
b. $p = 10 - q^2$ $p$ = [ ]

c. $5q - 4 = p$ $p$ = [ ]
d. $100 - q^3 = p$ $p$ = [ ]

e. $(3 + q)^2 = p$ $p$ = [ ]
f. $\frac{5 + q^3}{4} = p$ $p$ = [ ]

4. Complete the number pairs for each equation.

a. $t = 5s - 2$

| s | 1 | 2 | 3 | 4 | 5 |
|---|---|---|---|---|---|
| t | 3 | | | | |

b. $t = 3s^2 - 5$

| s | 1 | 2 | 3 | 4 | 5 |
|---|---|---|---|---|---|
| t | –2 | | | | |

5. Here a number sequence. What is the rule?

2, 5, 11, 23, 47, 95

The rule is ______________________________________________

6. Complete this number sequence.

0, 2, __________, 12, 20, 30, 42, __________

What would the 10th term be? __________

# 13 Units of measurement

## CAN YOU?

- Convert between standard units, using decimal notation to up to three decimal places.
- Convert between miles and kilometres.
- Solve problems involving units of time.

Remember that the number of kilometres will always be a larger number than the number of miles.

## SKILLS CHECK

To convert between metric units, multiply or divide by 10, 100 or 1000. To convert between units of time remember: there are 60 seconds in 1 minute, 60 minutes in 1 hour, 24 hours in 1 day, 7 days in 1 week, 52 weeks in 1 year, and so on. To convert a time given in a smaller unit to a larger unit, divide. To convert a time given in a larger unit to a smaller one, multiply.

| | |
|---|---|
| 420 minutes = [ ] hours | 25 days = [ ] hours |
| *Given smaller unit so divide* | *Given larger unit so multiply* |
| *420 ÷ 60 = 7 hours* | *25 × 24 = 600 hours* |

To convert between miles and kilometres, remember that there are approximately 1.6km to every mile. So to change a distance in miles to km you can multiply by 1.6 and to convert from a distance in km to miles you can divide by 1.6.

Approximately how many miles is 20 km?
*20 km ≈ ? miles*

***Using division***
*Divide 20 by 1.6 (the same as dividing 200 by 16).*
*200 ÷ 16 = 12.5 miles*

***Using scaling/ratio***
*You know 1.6 km ≈ 1 mile*
*so 16 km ≈ 10 miles (multiplying the previous line by 10)*
*4 km ≈ 2.5 miles (dividing the previous line by 4)*
*so 20 km ≈ 12.5 miles (adding 10 miles and 2.5 miles)*

***Using tables***
*To convert km to miles you can divide by 8 and then multiply by 5 (in either order). So to find 20 km in miles calculate*
*20 ÷ 8 × 5 or 20 × 5 ÷ 8 It is easier here to do the second calculation.*
*20 × 5 ÷ 8 = 100 ÷ 8 = 12.5 miles*

Use the same approach to convert speed such as km per hour to miles per hour. However, if the speed is given with a different time unit, such as km per minute, you'll need to change to multiply or divide by the time unit.

Change 8km per minute to miles per hour.

8km every minute is 8km × 60 every hour = 480km per hour

480km per hour *480 ÷ 1.6 ≈ 300 miles per hour*

## PRACTICE

1. Fill in the missing numbers.

a. 8 hours = [ ] minutes

b. 240 seconds = [ ] minutes

c. 8mm = [ ] m

d. 240kg = [ ] g

e. 8l = [ ] ml

f. 240 hours = [ ] days

2. Circle the length equivalent to 5cm.

500mm 0.05km 5m 0.5m 0.05m

3. Circle the length equivalent to 150mm.

1.5cm 0.015km 0.015m 0.15m

4. Circle the length equivalent to 0.36km.

36cm 36,000cm 36m 3600m

5. a. Approximately how many miles is 64km? [ ] miles

b. Approximately how many miles is 480km? [ ] miles

c. Approximately how many miles is 120km? [ ] miles

6. a. Approximately how many kilometres is 7 miles? [ ] km

b. Approximately how many kilometres is 12 miles? [ ] km

c. Approximately how many kilometres is 500 miles? [ ] km

7. Sarah says,

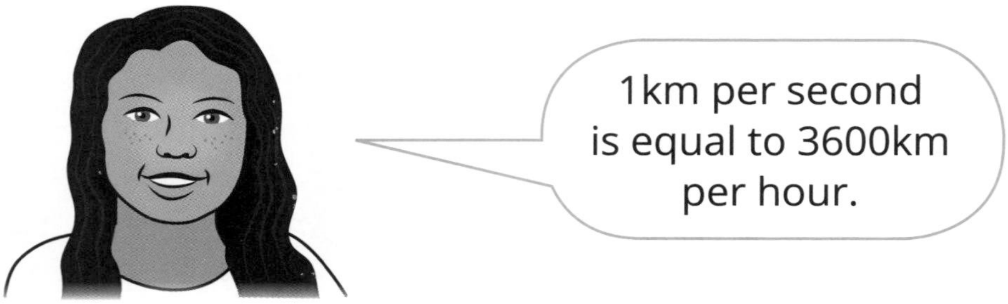

1km per second
is equal to 3600km
per hour.



Explain why she is correct.

______________________________________________

______________________________________________

8. 960km per hour is approximately the same speed as 600 miles per hour.
Give this speed in:

a. kilometres per **minute**. [ ] km/min

b. miles per **minute**. [ ] miles per minute

9. Change this speed into miles per hour.

8000 metres per minute [ ] miles per hour

10. Change this speed into km per hour.

3 miles per minute [ ] km per hour

# 14 Measurement problems

## CAN YOU?

- Solve problems involving the calculation of units of measure, using decimal notation up to three decimals places where appropriate.
- Calculate the duration of an event using appropriate units of time, including 12- and 24-hour clocks, timetables and calendars.

## SKILLS CHECK

When solving **measurement problems** with a 'Show your method' answer box, always clearly show the calculations you are attempting, as you might score a mark for choosing the correct one, even if your answer is incorrect. If using standard written methods of calculation, include all carrying marks and remember to estimate and to check your answer at the end. Look at the units of measurement carefully and convert any so that they are all in the same unit, if possible.

Sook has a length of ribbon that is 1.7 metres long.
She cuts off a piece that is 34 centimetres long.
What length of ribbon is left?

*Change to the same units (either metres or centimetres)*
*1.7m is 170cm* *170 – 34 = 136*

*Remember to give the unit in your answer: 136cm or 1.36m.*

To work out the lengths of sides of rectilinear shapes (shapes made from rectangles) look for sets of sides that are parallel. Then use addition, subtraction, multiplication or division to work out missing lengths.

Find the length of $x$ and $y$.

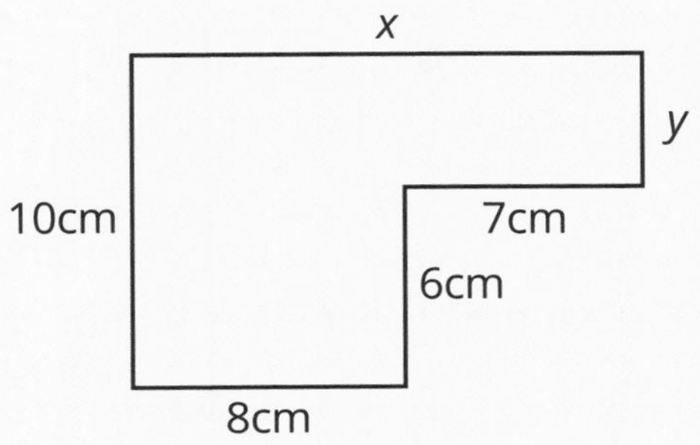

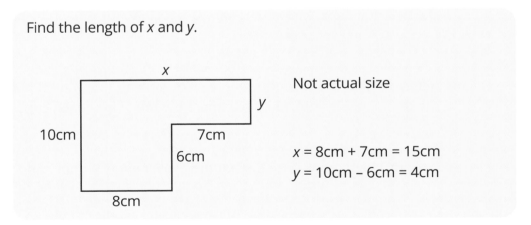

Not actual size

$x$ = 8cm + 7cm = 15cm
$y$ = 10cm – 6cm = 4cm

The identical bricks in this design each have a length of 22.5cm.
Find the length *m*.

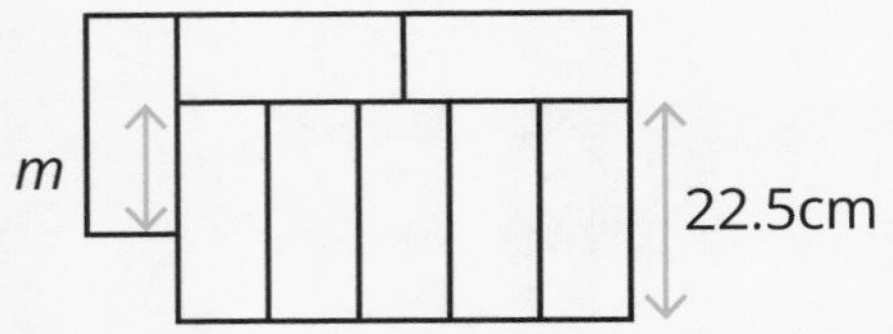


*Notice in the design that* ***two lengths*** *are equal to* ***five widths****, so the width of one brick is (22.5 × 2) ÷ 5 = 9cm.*

*So m is 22.5 − 9 = 13.5cm.*

## PRACTICE

1. Solve each problem.

   a. Piotr adapts a recipe to make a pie. The recipe says he needs 800g flour and 0.48kg of butter. He only has 600g of flour. How many grams of butter should he use with it?

   ______ g

   b. A 3.8m piece of ribbon is cut into four equal strips. What is the length of each strip in centimetres?

   ______ cm

   c. Salma runs a 10km race. After 4.5km she stops and walks for 350m. After walking, how far does she still have to go to the end of the race?

   ______

   d. A fizzy drink is sold in 2 litre bottles. For a party, Kim buys 3 bottles and shares the drink equally into 15 large cups. How much is in each cup?

   ______

   e. A digital clock shows 21:47. What time will it show 4 hours and 32 minutes later?

   ______

   f. Today is Wednesday 21 June. Sam is going on holiday in 25 days time. On what day of the week is he going on holiday?

   ______

2. Find the length of the sides marked with a letter in these diagrams.

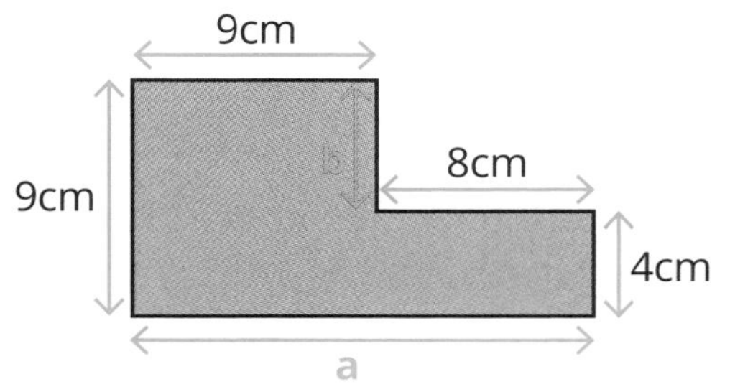


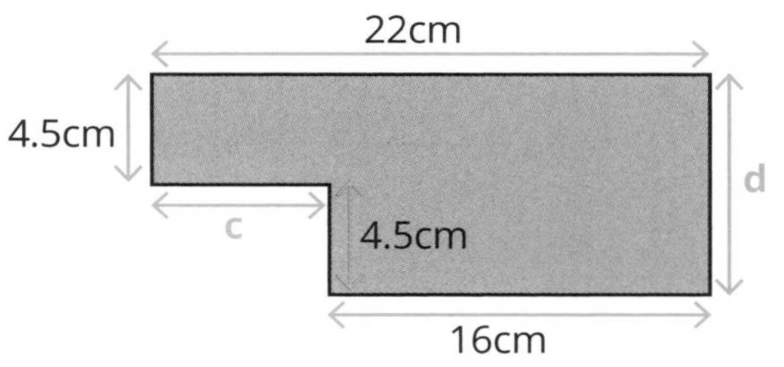


a = ☐ b = ☐ c = ☐ d = ☐

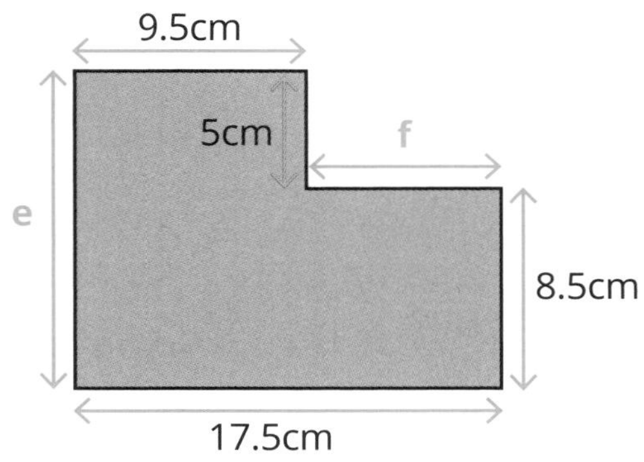


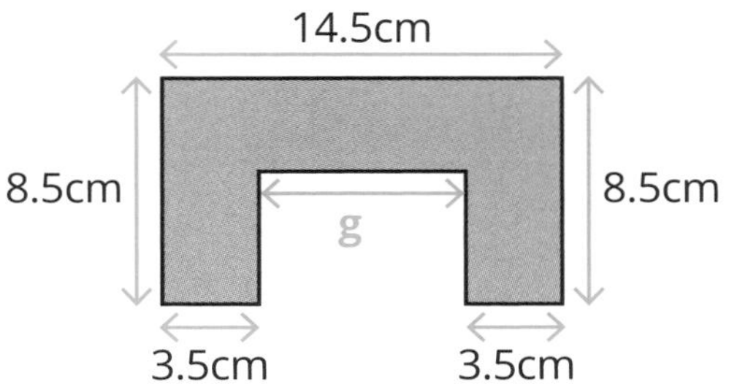


e = ☐ f = ☐ g = ☐

3. The design is made from identical rectangles with length 10.5cm and width 6.5cm. Find the length of *x* and *y*.

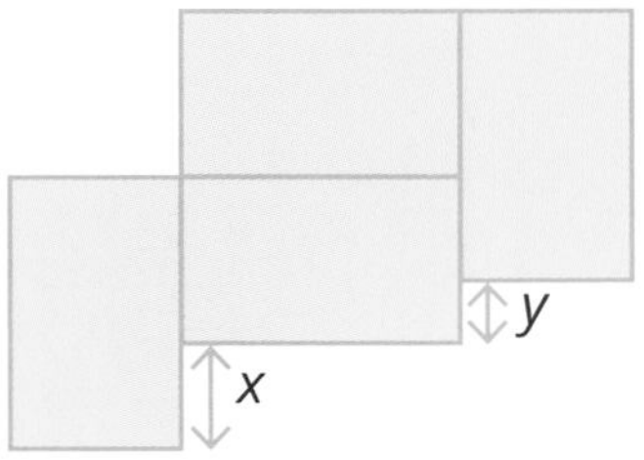


*x* = ☐ *y* = ☐

4. This design is made from identical right-angled triangles with sides of 5cm, 12cm and 13cm. Find the length of *x*.

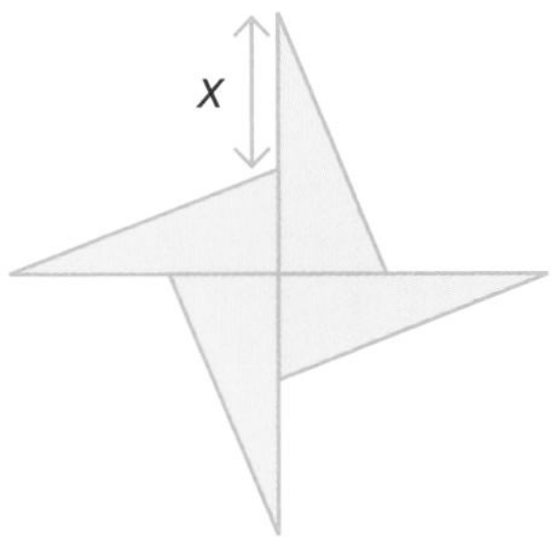


*x* = ☐ cm

# 15 Area and perimeter

## CAN YOU?

- **Find the perimeter of compound shapes where all the side lengths are known or can be easily determined.**
- **Use formulae to find areas and perimeters of rectilinear shapes and other shapes including triangles and parallelograms.**
- **Begin to work out a formula for the area of a trapezium.**

For some questions it may be easier to find the area of a larger area and subtract part of it instead.

## SKILLS CHECK

For **area** and **perimeter** it is important to be able to deduce the lengths of unmarked sides. Once you know the lengths of all the sides you can work out the perimeter and area. Use formulae such as these, if you can.

| | |
|---|---|
| Perimeter of rectangle with length $l$ and width $w$ | $P = 2l + 2w$ or $P = 2(l + w)$ |
| Area of rectangle with length $l$ and width $w$ | $A = l \times w$ or $A = lw$ |
| Area of triangle with base $b$ and perpendicular height $h$ | $A = \frac{1}{2}b \times h$ or $A = \frac{1}{2}bh$ |
| Area of parallelogram with base $b$ and perpendicular height $h$ | $A = b \times h$ or $A = bh$ |

When you calculate the area of compound shapes (made from more than one shape): split the shape into parts, find the area of each separately and then add the answers together.

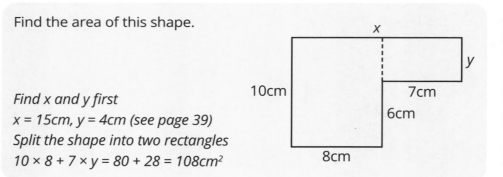

Find the area of this shape.

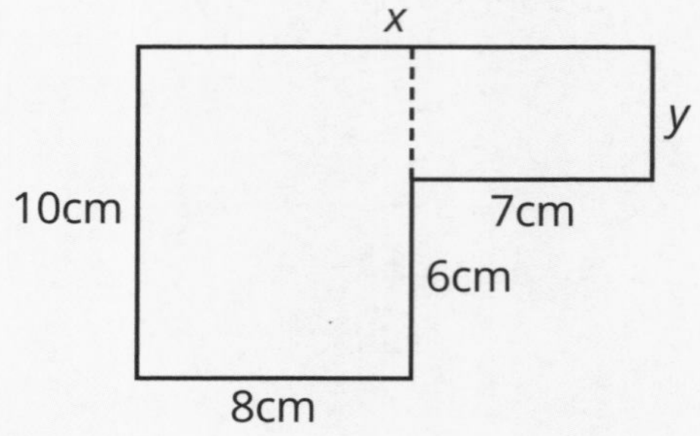


*Find x and y first*

*$x = 15$cm, $y = 4$cm (see page 39)*

*Split the shape into two rectangles*

*$10 \times 8 + 7 \times y = 80 + 28 = 108$cm$^2$*

A trapezium is made from joining a rectangle and two right-angled triangles, all of the same height. Write a formula for finding the area of this **trapezium**.

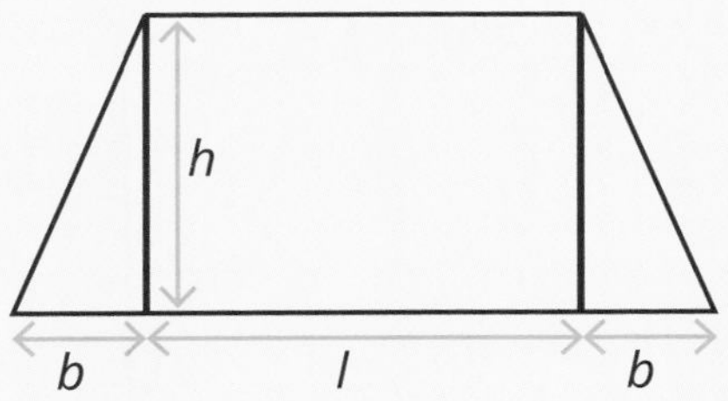


*Area of rectangle = lh* *Area of triangle =* $\frac{1}{2}bh$
*So area of this trapezium = lh +* $\frac{1}{2}bh + \frac{1}{2}bh$
*Simplify: A = lh + bh so A = h(l + b)*

*You can see from this diagram how moving one triangle makes the shape into a rectangle and it is easy then to see that the formula for its area is A = h(l + b).*

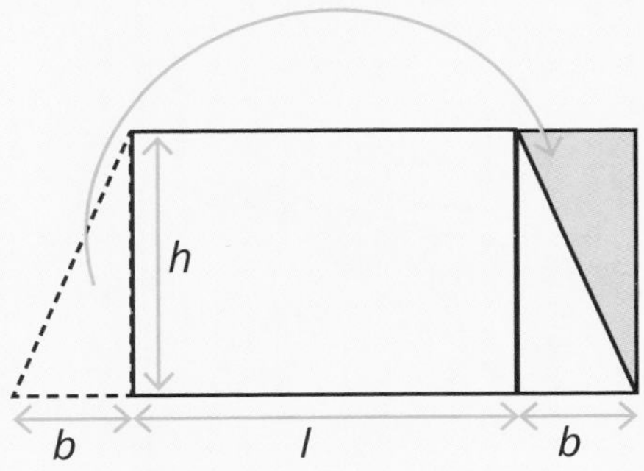


*Not every trapezium is symmetrical so this is not the general rule for trapeziums.*

## PRACTICE

1. Find the area and perimeter of each shape.

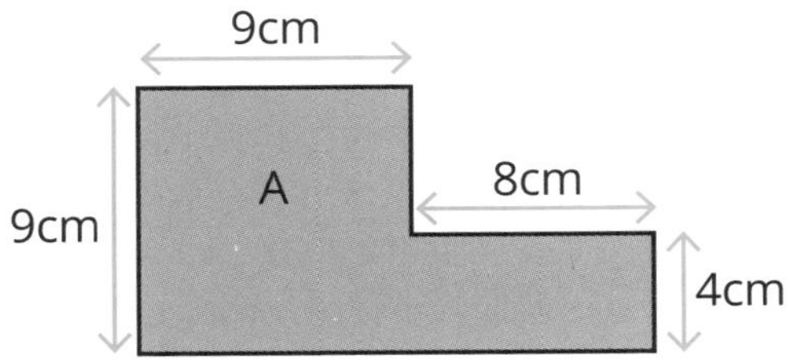


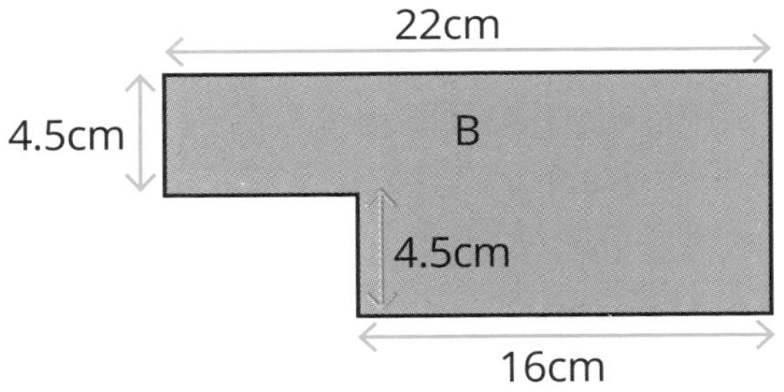


a. area = ______________________ $cm^2$

perimeter = ______________________ cm

b. area = ______________________ $cm^2$

perimeter = ______________________ cm

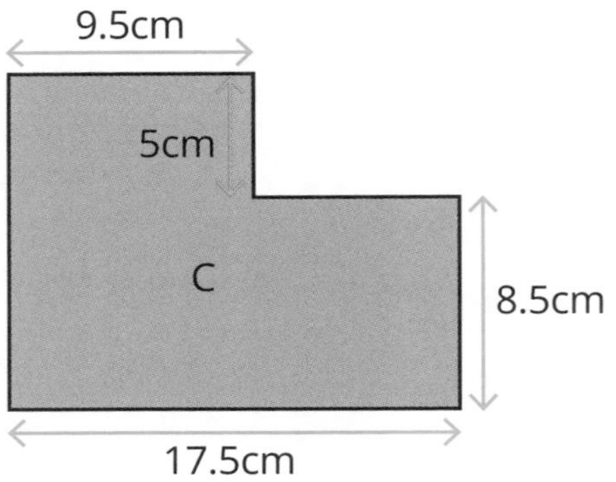


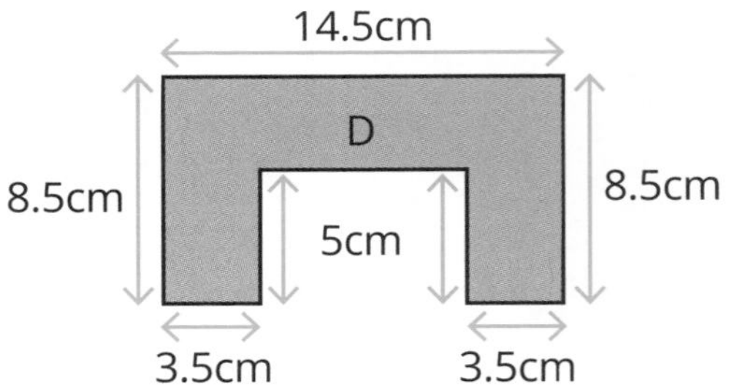


c. area = ______________ $cm^2$

perimeter = ______________ cm

d. area = ______________ $cm^2$

perimeter = ______________ cm

2. Find the difference between the areas of these two triangles and the difference between the perimeters of the two triangles.

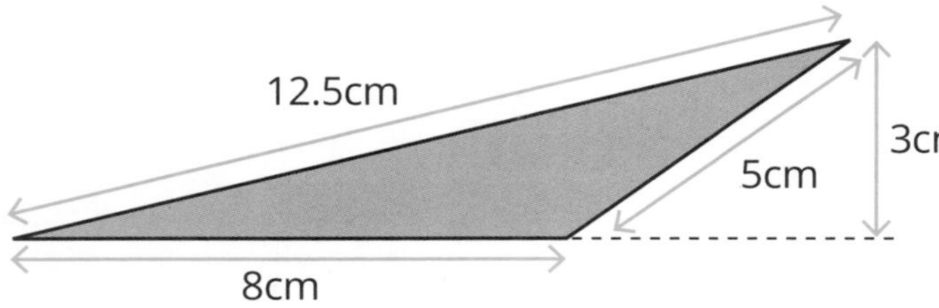


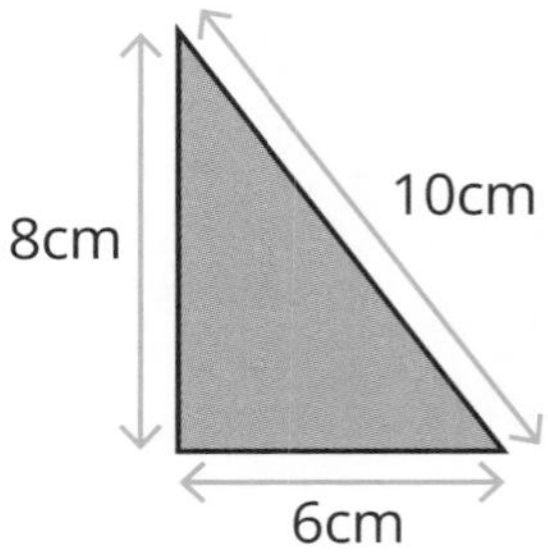


Difference between areas = ______________ $cm^2$

Difference between perimeters = ______________ cm

3. A trapezium is made from joining a rectangle and two **different** right-angled triangles, all of the same height. Write a formula for finding the area of this trapezium.

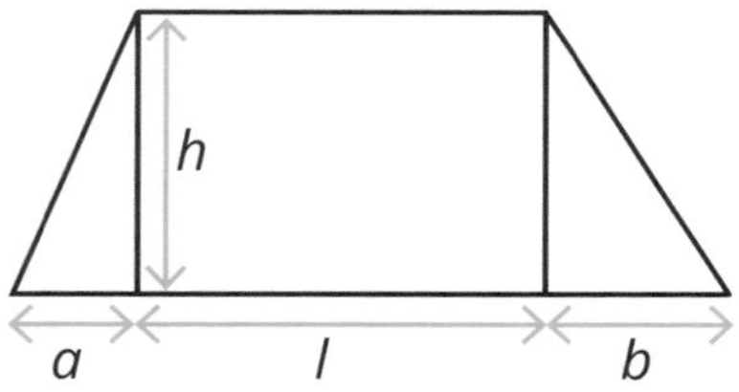


Area of the trapezium = ______________

4. A triangular corner is cut from a rhombus with sides of 6cm. The cut is made along the dotted line. Calculate the area of the trapezium part that remains.

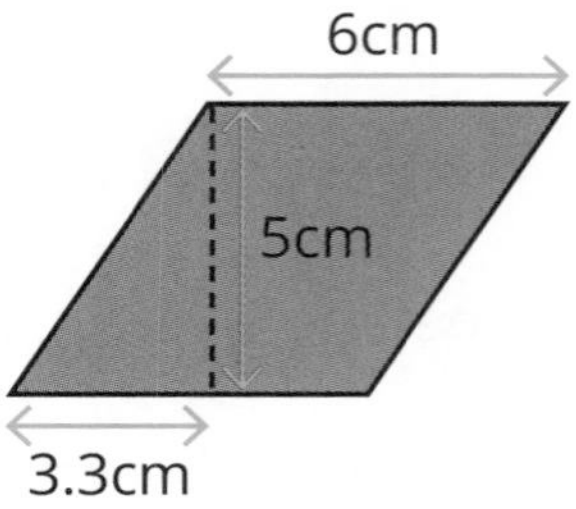


Area of the trapezium = ______________$cm^2$

16

# Volume

## CAN YOU?

- Calculate, estimate and compare volume of cubes and cuboids using standard units, including $cm^3$ and $m^3$.
- Use formulae for the volume of shapes.
- Deduce missing dimension of cuboids, given their volumes and some dimensions.

## SKILLS CHECK

To find the volume (V) of a cuboid with length ***l***, width ***w*** and height ***h***, multiply the length by the width by the height or use the formula $V = l \times w \times h$. Take note of the unit of the dimensions of the shapes, for example: whether they are in mm or cm.

Find the volume of each cuboid and say which two have the same volume.

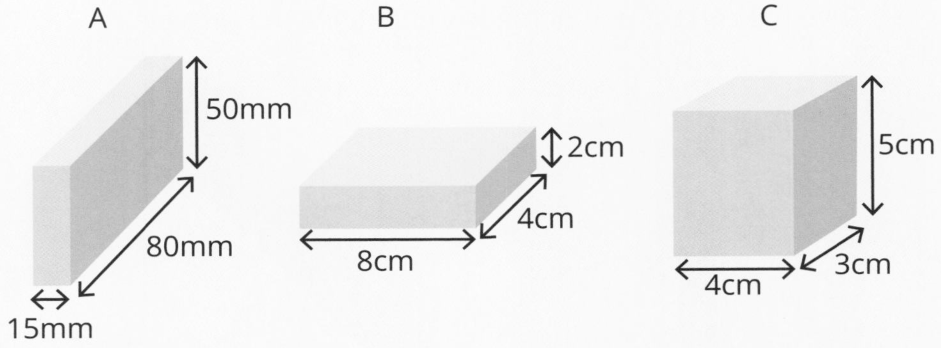


*Change all the lengths to be cm.*

| | |
|---|---|
| *Cuboid A in cm* | $V = 1.5 \times 8 \times 5 = 60cm^3$ |
| *Cuboid B in cm* | $V = 8 \times 4 \times 2 = 64cm^3$ |
| *Cuboid C in cm* | $V = 4 \times 3 \times 5 = 60cm^3$ |

*So A and C have the same volume.*

If the area of one face of the cuboid is known (in other words, two of the dimensions have already been multiplied) multiply this area by the remaining dimension.

Find the volume of a cuboid with a base area of $42cm^2$ and a height of 5cm.

*Multiply the area of the base by the height.*

$42 \times 5 = 210$ *Volume* $= 210cm^3$

## PRACTICE

1. Find the volume of each cuboid.

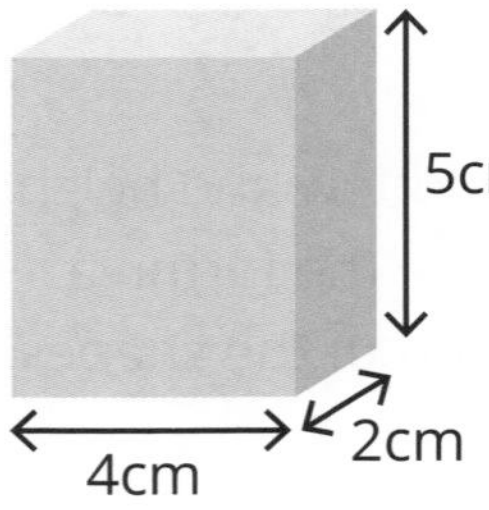


a. Volume = ____________

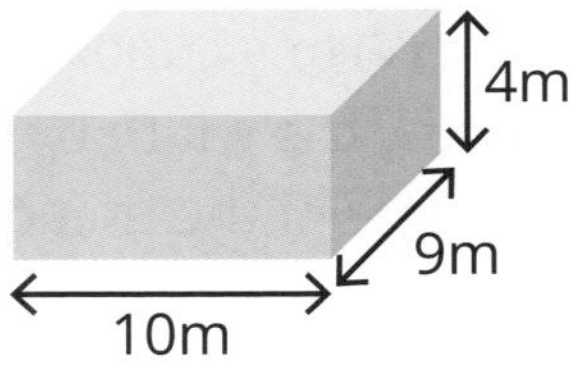


b. Volume = ____________

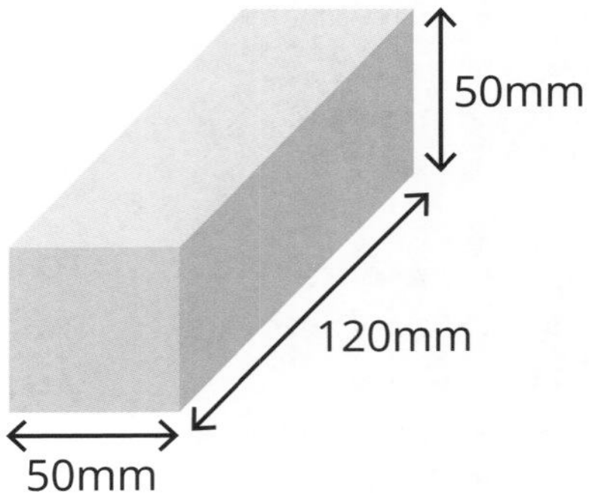


c. Volume = ____________

2. Find the missing length for each cuboid, given its volume. Give the correct unit of measurement in your answer.

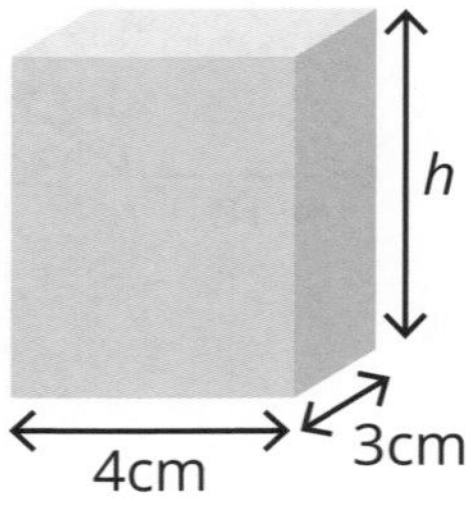


a. Volume = $48cm^3$

$h$ = ____________

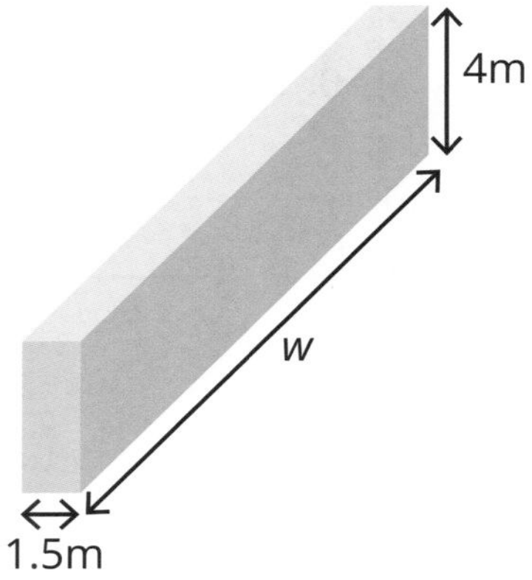


b. Volume = $60m^3$

$w$ = ____________

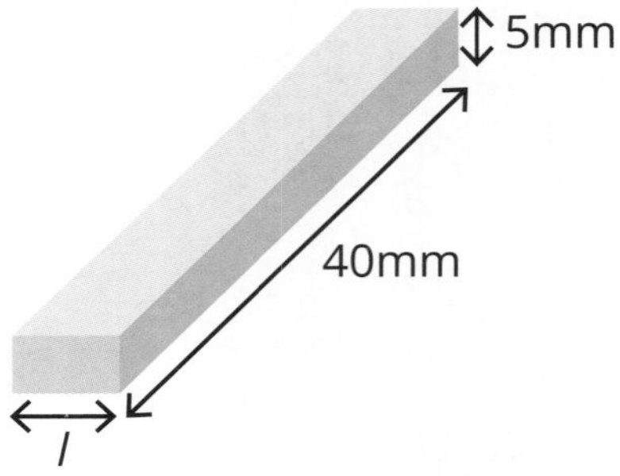


c. Volume = $1800mm^3$

$l$ = ____________

3. Solve these problems.

a. Jack joins 150 centimetre cubes together to make a cuboid. His cuboid has length $l$, width $w$ and height $h$. Write possible dimensions of his cuboid.

$l$ = ____________ $w$ = ____________ $h$ = ____________

b. The area of one face of a cube is $9cm^2$. What is the volume of the cube?

[ ] $cm^3$

c. A cuboid has a square base and a height that is twice its length. The square base has an area of $49cm^2$. Calculate the volume of the cuboid.

[ ] $cm^3$

17

# Properties of shapes

## CAN YOU?

- Compare and classify geometric shapes based on their properties.
- Know that the diameter of a circle is twice the radius and express the relationship between diameter and radius of a circle algebraically.
- Recognise and describe nets of 3D shapes.

## SKILLS CHECK

Make sure you understand the words in this box. Whenever you give written explanations, try to use the correct terms.

| |
|---|
| Perpendicular lines – at right angles to each other |
| Parallel lines – separated everywhere from each other by the same distance |
| Regular polygon – has both equal sides and equal angles |
| Equilateral triangle – a regular triangle (3 equal sides and 3 equal angles of 60°) |
| Isosceles triangle – has 2 equal sides and 2 equal angles |
| Scalene triangle – has no equal sides or angles |
| Vertex (plural: vertices) – the point on a shape where two or more sides or edges meet |
| Net – a pattern that you can cut and fold to make a model of a 3D shape |

The diameter of a circle is a straight line passing from side to side through its centre and the radius is the line going from the centre to its edge.

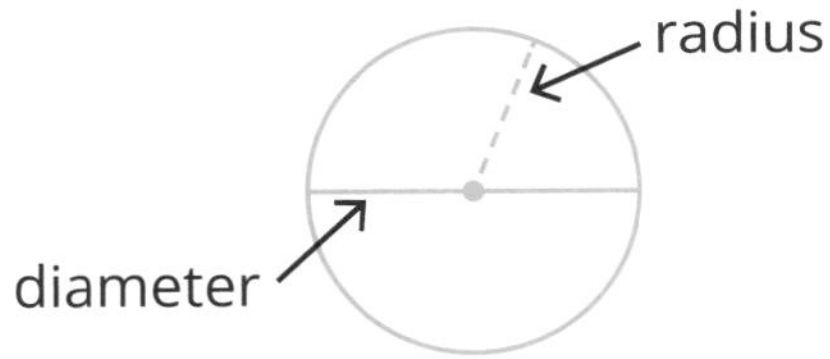


The circumference is the perimeter of the circle.

Remember that the radius is always half the length of the diameter.

This can be expressed using algebra as $d = 2r$ or $\frac{1}{2}d = r$.

The radius of a circle is 8cm. Give its diameter.
*d = 2r so double the radius to give the diameter of 16cm.*

Make sure you know the properties of these special quadrilaterals:

A **quadrilateral** with:

- one pair of parallel sides is a **trapezium**

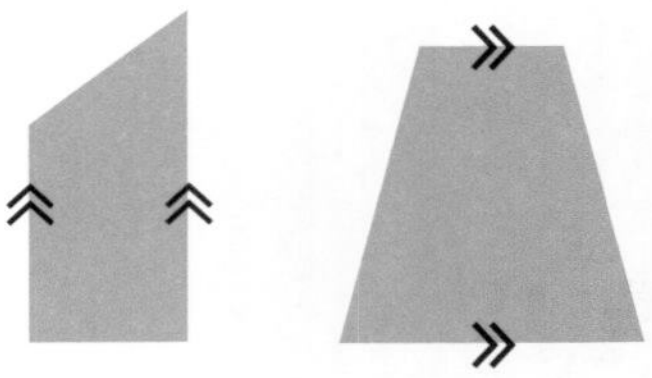

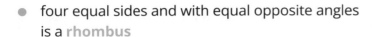

- two pairs of parallel sides and with equal opposite angles is a **parallelogram**

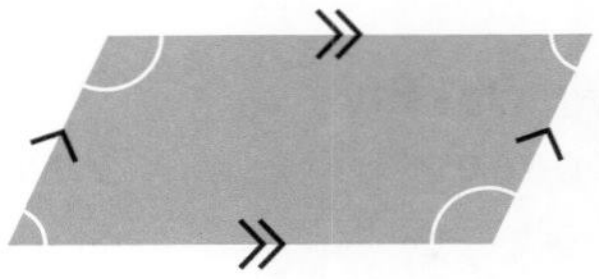

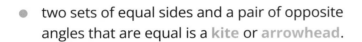

- four equal sides and with equal opposite angles is a **rhombus**

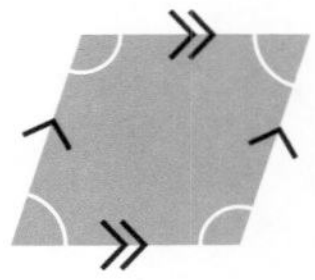

- two sets of equal sides and a pair of opposite angles that are equal is a **kite** or **arrowhead**.

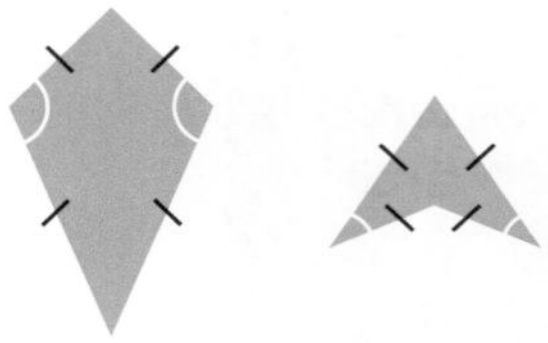

A shape has 4 straight sides, 2 lines of symmetry and no right angles.
Which of these names could correctly describe it?

**rectangle** **kite** **parallelogram** **trapezium** **rhombus** **square** **quadrilateral**

*This shape is a rhombus.*

## PRACTICE

1. Write the name of a shape to match each description.

a. 2D shape
4 straight sides
No parallel sides
1 line of symmetry
2 equal angles

b. 2D shape
3 straight sides
1 right angle
2 angles of 45°
1 line of symmetry

c. 2D shape
8 straight sides
4 pairs of parallel sides
8 equal angles
8 lines of symmetry

d. 3D shape
2 identical triangular faces
3 rectangular faces
6 vertices

e. 3D shape
6 rectangular faces
8 vertices
12 edges

f. 3D shape
4 triangular faces
6 edges
4 vertices

2. A square-based pyramid has 5 vertices and 5 faces.

How many edges does it have?

3. A circle with a radius of 7cm has a circumference of 22cm.
It is cut in half along its diameter to make two semicircles.

What is the perimeter of one of the semicircles? cm

4. The diameter of a circle is *d* mm. Write an equation to show the radius, *r*, of this circle in terms of *d*.

*r* = ____________________

5. Name the 3D shape each of these nets would fold to make.
Then tick those that are prisms.

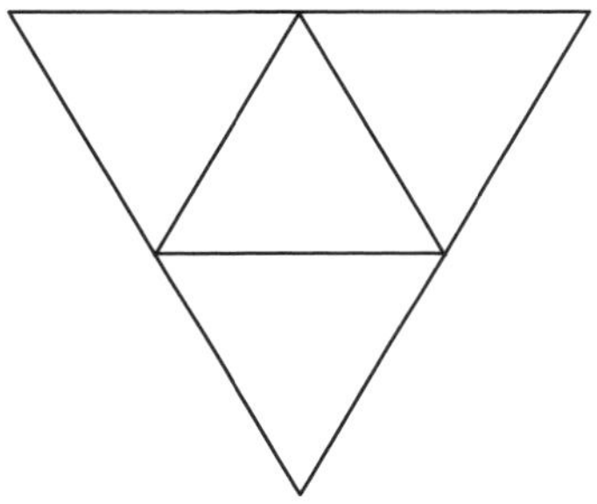

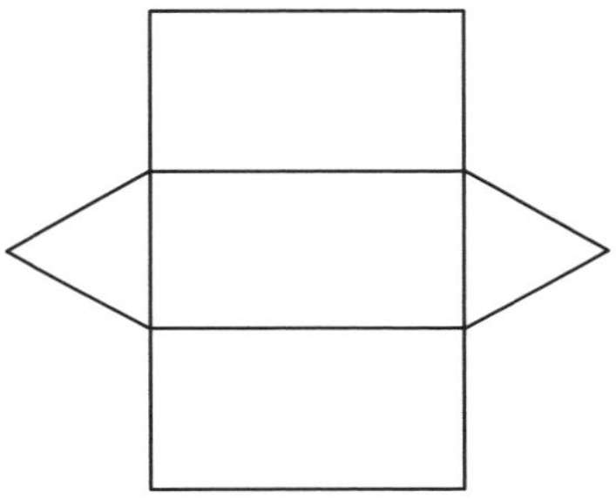

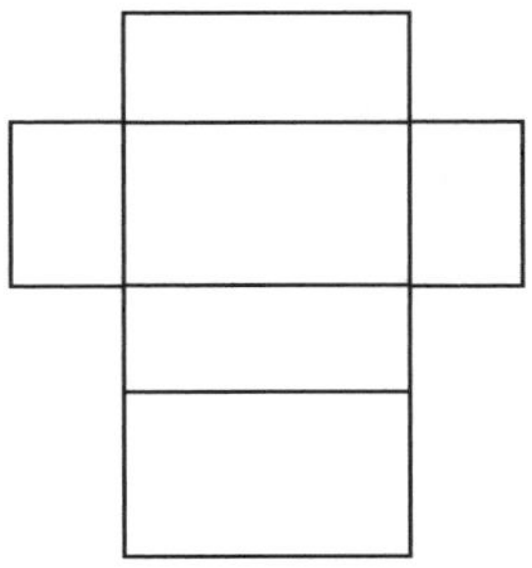

a. ____________________ b. ____________________ c. ____________________

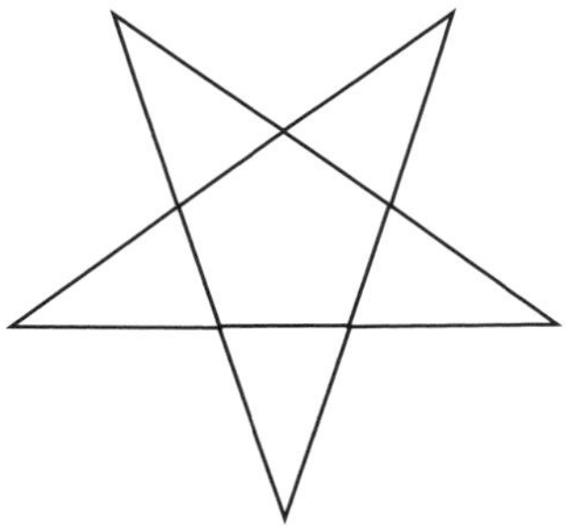

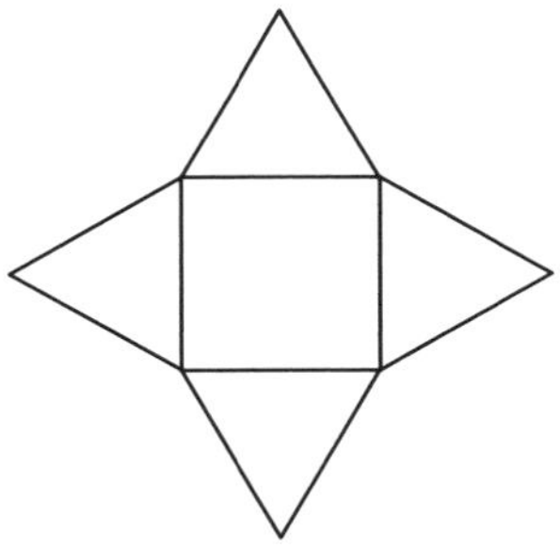

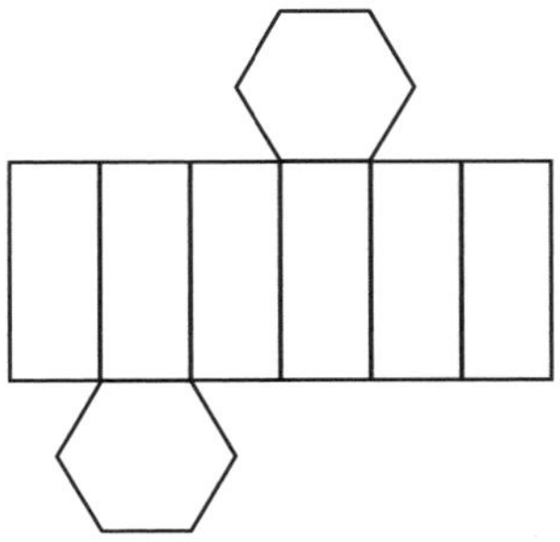

d. ____________________ e. ____________________ f. ____________________

18

# Angles

## CAN YOU?

- **Recognise angles where they meet at a point, are on a straight line, or are vertically opposite.**
- **Find unknown angles in any triangle, quadrilaterals and regular polygons and in more complex diagrams involving several lines.**
- **Use algebra to show unknown angles, for example $c = 180 - (a + b)$.**

## SKILLS CHECK

Acute angles are greater than 0° but less than 90°.

Obtuse angles are greater than 90° but less than 180°.

Reflex angles are greater than 180° but less than 360°.

The sum of the angles:

- in any triangle is 180°
  $a + b + c = 180°$

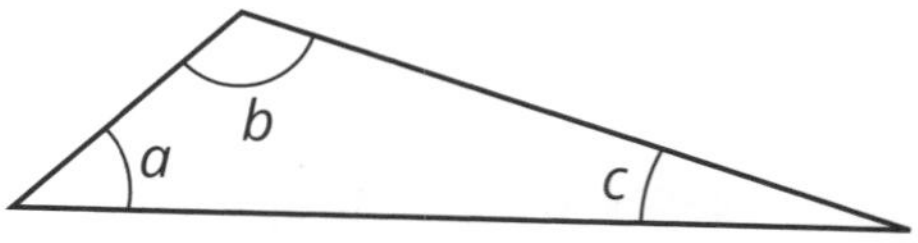


- in any quadrilateral is 360°
  $d + e + f + g = 360°$

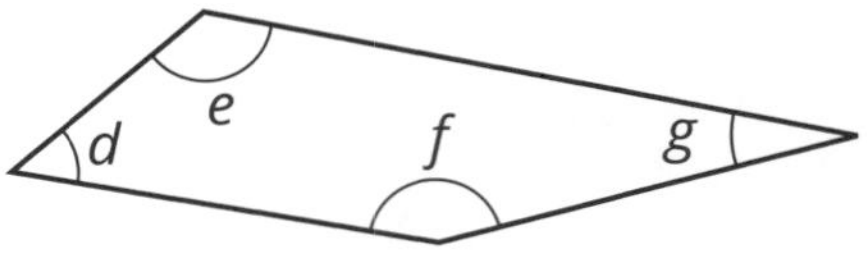


- along a straight line is 180°
  $h + i + j = 180°$

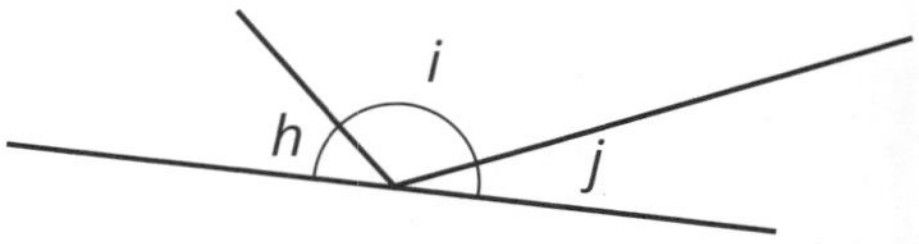


- about a point is 360°
  $k + l + m + n + p = 360°$

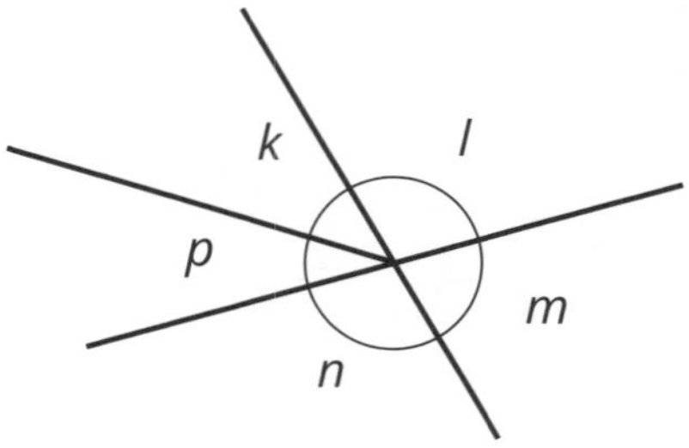


Remember also that if straight lines cross, the opposite angles are equal.

Calculate the sizes of angles *m* and *n* and explain how you worked them out. State what type of angles *m* and *n* are.

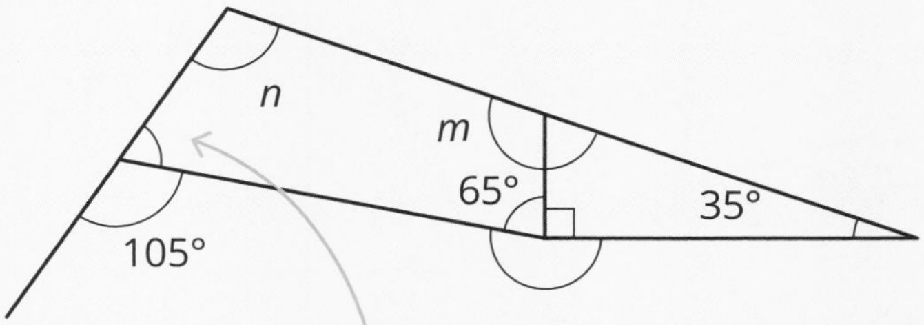


NOT TO SCALE

***Explanation:***

*First I subtracted 105° from 180° (angles on a straight line). 180° – 105° = 75°*

*As the angles in a triangle add to 180° I found the third angle of the triangle by subtracting 90° and 35° from 180°. 180° – (90° + 35°) = 55°*

*m + 55° = 180° (angles on a straight line), so m = 180° – 55° = 125°.*

*n + m + 75° + 65° = 360° (angles in a quadrilateral) and m is 125°, so n = 95°.*

*Both m and n are obtuse angles.*

## PRACTICE

1. Calculate and write in the size of each unmarked angle. (diagrams are not to scale)

a.

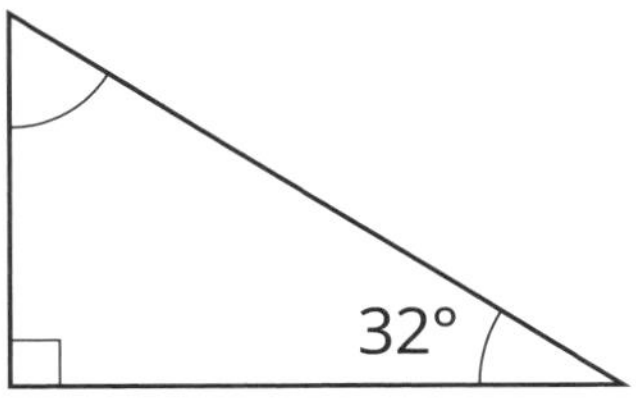


b.

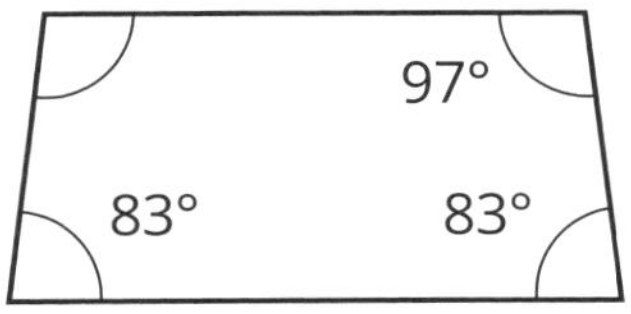


c.

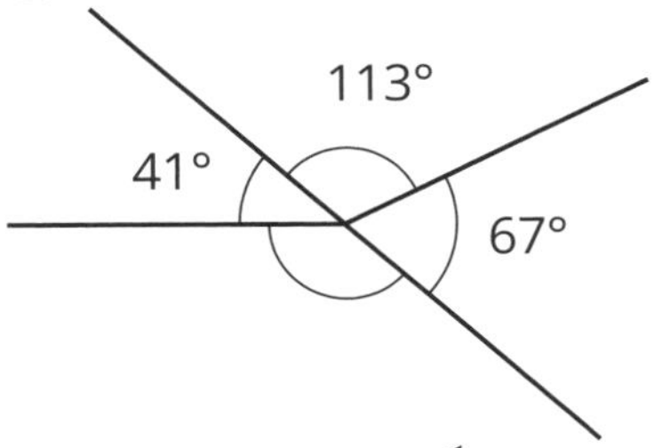


d.

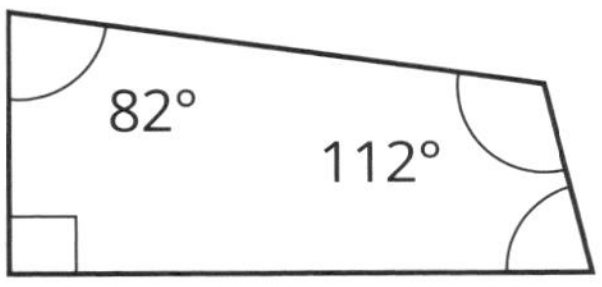


e.

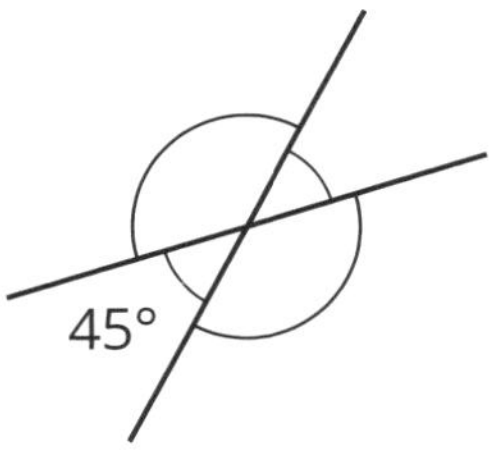


f.

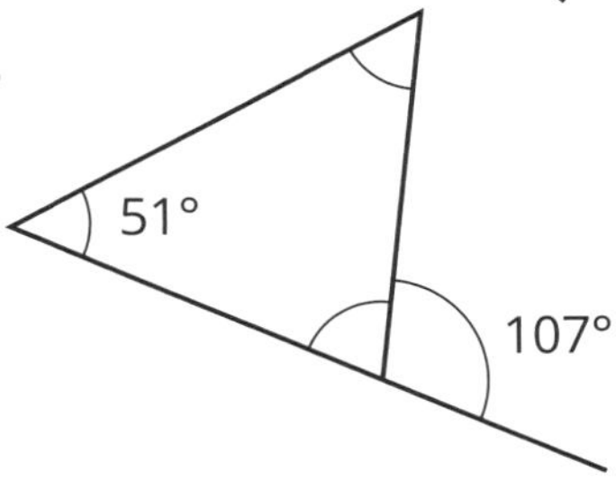


2. In the diagrams above, circle all the obtuse angles.

3. Calculate the unknown angles and explain how you worked them out (diagrams are not to scale).

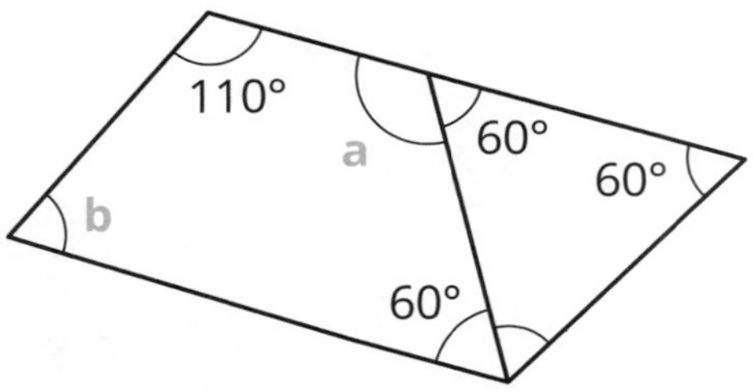


a = ______ b = ______

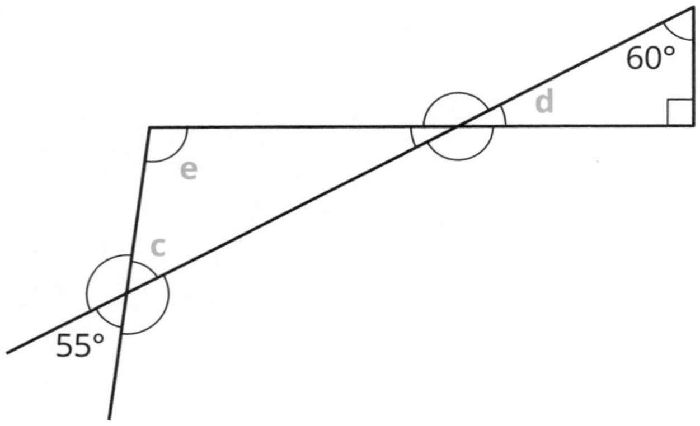


c = ______ d = ______

e = ______

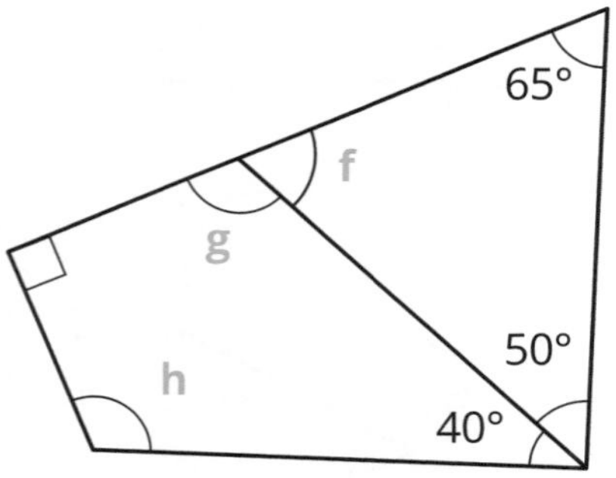


f = ______ g = ______

h = ______

19

# Coordinate grids and transformations

## CAN YOU?

- Describe positions on the full coordinate grid (all four quadrants).
- Translate simple shapes on the coordinate plane and reflect them in the axes.
- Express translations and reflections algebraically.

*x always comes before y when writing coordinates.*

## SKILLS CHECK

There are patterns in the coordinates of points along straight lines (*x*,*y*).

For vertical lines, the *x*-coordinates of the points are the same.

For horizontal lines, the *y*-coordinates of the points are the same.

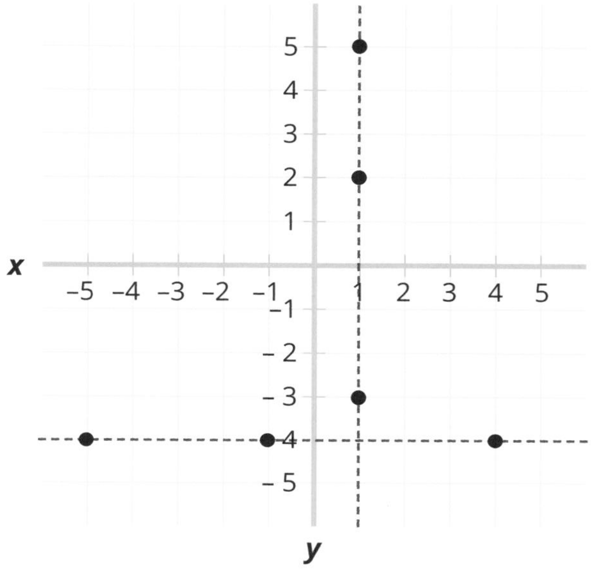


Write the coordinates of the marked points on:

a. the vertical dotted line *(1,5) (1,2) (1,–3)* $x = 1$

b. the horizontal dotted line *(4,–4) (−1,–4) (–5,–4)* $y = -4$

These patterns can be used to work out unknown coordinates of vertices of some rectangles.

A square has vertices at the points (–2,–4) (–2,3) (5,3) and *(a,b)*.
Find *a* and *b*.

*A vertical side goes from (–**2**,–4) to (–**2**,3) with length 7 squares (from –4 to 3).*

*A horizontal side goes from (–2,**3**) to (5,**3**) with length 7 squares (from –2 to 5).*

*To find the missing coordinates, either translate the point (–2,–4) 7 squares to the right by adding 7 to the x-coordinate to give (5,–4) or translate the point (5,3) 7 squares down by subtracting 7 from the y-coordinate to give (5,–4).*

To translate (slide) a shape:

- horizontally change the ***x***-coordinate in all pairs of coordinates
- vertically change the ***y***-coordinate in all pairs of coordinates
- diagonally change both ***x*** and ***y*** in all pairs of coordinates

To reflect a shape in the:

- ***y***-axis change the ***x***-coordinate for each vertex from positive to negative (or vice versa). Zero stays the same.
- ***x***-axis change the ***y***-coordinate for each vertex from positive to negative (or vice versa). Zero stays the same.

A triangle has coordinates (−2,4) (2,3) and (−1,0). Write the new coordinates:

a. after a reflection in the *x*-axis
b. after a translation of 4 right, 3 down.

*a. Change the y-coordinates (zero doesn't change) (–2,–4) (2,–3) and (–1,0).*
*b. Add 4 to the x-coordinates, subtract 3 from the y-coordinates (2,1) (6,0) and (3,–3).*

## PRACTICE

1. The coordinates in each set are points along a straight line.

   Write whether each line is horizontal or vertical.

   a. (−3,−2) (3,−2) (0,−2) (5,−2) ______________________

   b. (−1,−1) (−1,−4) (−1,0) (−1,−2) ______________________

2. Each set of coordinates show the vertices of a rectangle. Complete the missing values.

a. (0,–3) (0,0) (4,0) ( _______ , _______ )

b. (–4,1) (–4,4) (2,4) ( _______ , _______ )

c. (3,4) (3,–2) (–1,–2) ( _______ , _______ )

d. (5,–4) (–4,–4) (–4,4) ( _______ , _______ )

3. (−1,0) (1,−4) (5,−2) are the positions of three vertices of a square.

a. Plot them on the grid and complete the square.

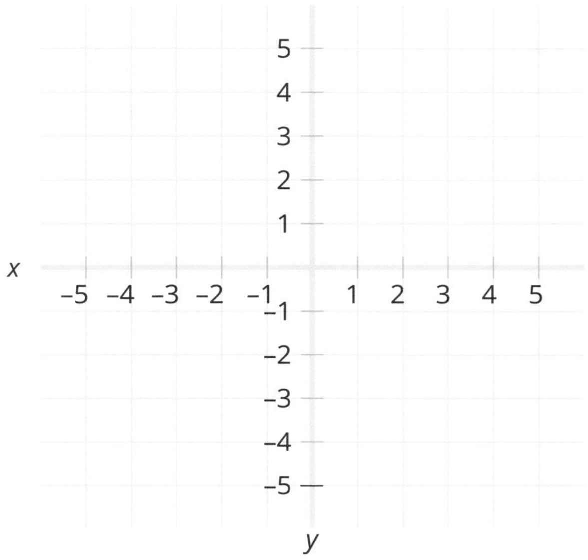


b. Give the coordinates of the **fourth** vertex. ( _______ , _______ )

c. Draw a new square showing the position of this square after a translation **2 left and 3 up**.

d. Write the coordinates of the new square.

( _______ , _______ ) ( _______ , _______ ) ( _______ , _______ ) ( _______ , _______ )

4. A triangle has these coordinates (–2,2) (–1,1) (−4,1). Write the new coordinates:

a. after a reflection in the *x*-axis.

( _______ , _______ ) ( _______ , _______ ) ( _______ , _______ )

b. after a reflection in the *y*-axis.

( _______ , _______ ) ( _______ , _______ ) ( _______ , _______ )

c. after a translation of 6 right, 4 down.

( _______ , _______ ) ( _______ , _______ ) ( _______ , _______ )

# 20 Statistics

## CAN YOU?

- **Complete, read and interpret information presented in tables, charts and graphs.**
- **Interpret and construct pie charts and line graphs and use these to solve problems.**
- **Calculate and interpret the mean as an average.**

## SKILLS CHECK

Remember, to find the **mean** average of a set of values, find the total and then divide by the number of values.

mean = total ÷ number of values

If given the mean, you can find missing values.

mean × number of values = total

Find the mean heights of these five boys.
0.79m, 1.03m, 1.04m, 1.32m, 1.47m

*0.79 + 1.03 + 1.04 + 1.32 + 1.47 = 5.65*
*5.65 ÷ 5 (boys) = 1.13*
*Mean height = 1.13m*

The mean heights of five girls is 1.1m.

0.78m, [ ], 1.2m, 1.32m, 1.4m

*1.1 × 5 (girls) = 5.5 so the total of the values is 5.5m. Subtract the known values from this to find the missing value.*
*5.5 – 0.78 – 1.2 – 1.32 – 1.4 = 0.8*
*The missing height is 0.8m.*

When using pie charts note how many people or items the whole pie represents and remember that this is 360°. If the whole is 120 people, each person will be shown as 360° ÷ 120 = 3°. If the whole is 90 items, each item will be shown as 360° ÷ 90 = 4° and so on. Once you know this, the size of each slice of pie (segment) can be calculated. If each person is 3° then a 27° slice represents 9 people.

This table shows how 40 children get to school.

| Ways of getting to school | Number of children |
|---|---|
| Car | 19 |
| Bus | 10 |
| Cycle | 5 |
| Walk | 4 |
| Scooter | 2 |

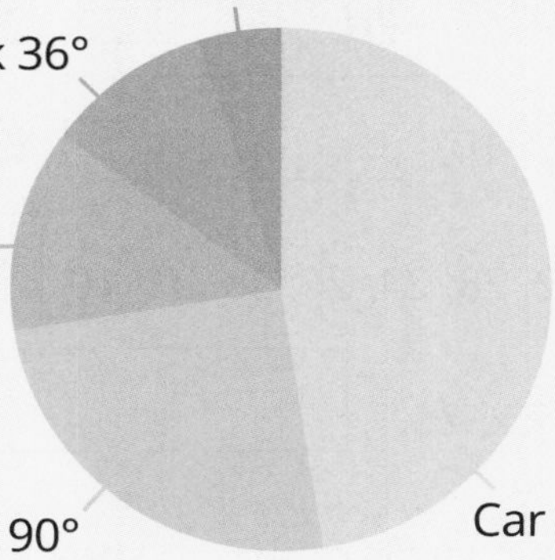


A pie chart is to be drawn of this data.

What size of segment of a pie chart will represent the proportion of girls that a. go by bus b. go by car?

Then draw the pie chart. The whole is 40 children.
360° ÷ 40 = 9°, so each child is 9°.
a. 10 children go by bus, 10 × 9° = 90°
b. 19 children go by car, 19 × 9° = 171°

The size of each segment can be worked out in the same way. Use an angle measurer (protractor) to measure and draw the angles correctly.

## PRACTICE

1. Find the mean of each set of values.

a. 5, 8, 4, 7, 5, 7, 5, 7 mean = ☐

b. 3.5, 4.5, 2.5, 3.5, 4.5, 4, 2 mean = ☐

c. 2.1, 2.6, 2.4, 2.0, 1.9 mean = ☐

2. The mean of each data set is 25. Find the missing value from each set.

a. 25, 27, 23, [ ], 27

b. 40, 10, [ ], 55, 45, 15, 15, 5

c. 22, 28, 24, 26, 30, 21, 19, [ ], 26, 31

d. 25.2, 25.1, [ ], 24.6

3. A pie chart is drawn to show the proportion of matches a football team won, lost or drew. The pie chart represents 72 matches.

a. How many degrees in the pie chart should be used to represent each match?

[ ]°

b. One third of the pie chart represents matches drawn. What is the angle of this segment of the pie chart?

[ ]°

c. Calculate how many matches were drawn. [ ]

d. The segment showing the number of matches won has an angle of 150°. Calculate how many matches were won.

[ ]

4. This pie chart shows the proportion of votes five candidates got in an election. In total 180 votes were cast. Complete the table to show the number of votes each person got.

| Candidate | Angle of segment | Number of votes |
|---|---|---|
| Mr R. Brown | | |
| Ms J. Patel | | |
| Mrs L. Nagy | | |
| Ms J. Connors | | |
| Mr F. Fox | | |

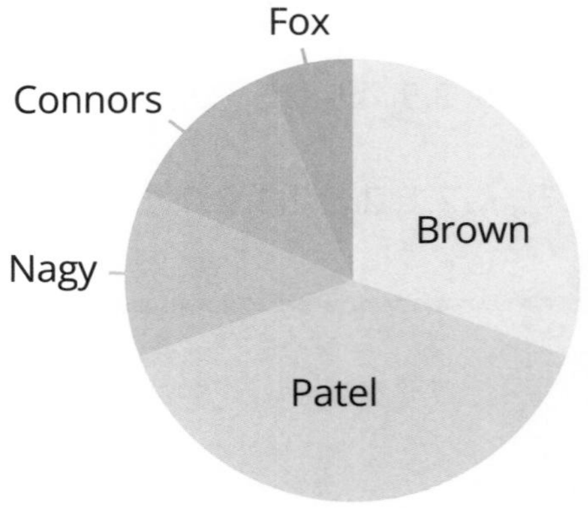

# Answers

The answers are given below. They are referenced by page number and question number. The answers usually only include the information the children are expected to give. There may be some places where the answers vary or multiple answers are acceptable, these are marked as such. Note that in some places, answers will be varied and subjective from child to child, and a fair degree of marker discretion and interpretation is needed, particularly if children's understanding and skills have to be deduced from their answers.

| Page | Q | Answers |
|---|---|---|
| 7 | 1 | Note that, when writing large numbers you don't have to use commas, you can just use spaces and will still get your answered marked correct, eg 7,000,000 or 7 000 000. Both will be marked the same.<br>a. seventy thousand seven hundred and seven<br>b. seven million, ten thousand and nine |
| | 2 | a. 14 b. 1995 c. 59,400 |
| | 3 | 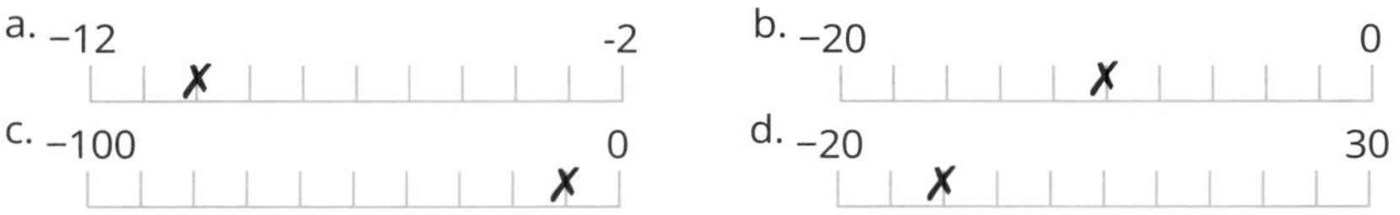 |
| 8 | 4 | a. 69,993 b. 396,000 c. 1,999,980 |
| | 5 | a. 218,000 rounds to 220,000<br>b. 1,554,999 rounds to 1,550,000<br>c. 7,145,000 rounds to 7,150,000 |
| | 6 | a. −1 and 23<br>b. −19 and 61<br>c. −25 and 7 |
| | 7 | 49,500 and 50,499 |
| 10 | 1 | 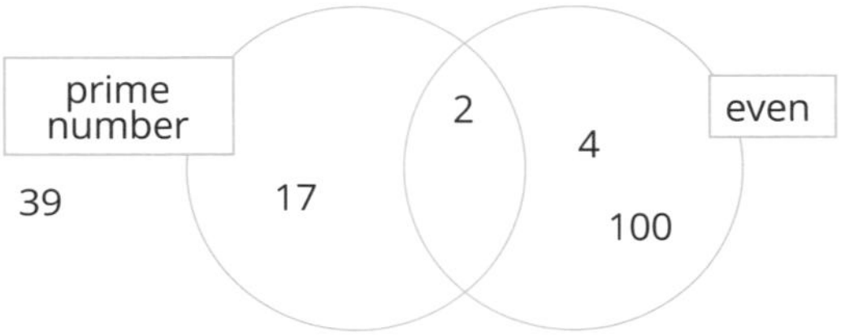 |
| | 2 | There are many acceptable answers, using cube numbers: 1, 8, 27, 64, 125…<br>prime numbers: 2, 3, 5, 7, 11, 13, 17, 19, 23, 29, 31, 37, 41, 43, 47, 53, 59, 61, 67, 71, 73, 79, 83, 89, 97…<br>square numbers: 1, 4, 9, 16, 25, 36, 49, 64, 81, 100…<br>Example answers:<br>2 (prime) + 2 (prime) = 4 (square)<br>25 (square) + 2 (prime) = 27 (cube) |
| 11 | 3 | 24 |
| | 4 | a = 56 b = 48 |
| | 5 | 54 = 2 × 3 × 3 × 3<br>90 = 2 × 3 × 3 × 5<br>Highest common factor = 2 × 3 × 3 = 18 |
| | 6 | a. 21 b. 45 |

# ANSWERS

| Page | Q | Answers |
|---|---|---|
| 13 | 1 | a. 640,000 b. 200,000 c. 45,000 d. 780,000<br>e. 56,000 f. 2,400,000 g. 80,000 h. 700,000 |
| | 2 | × \| 70 \| 90<br>40 \| 2800 \| 3600<br>70 \| 4900 \| 6300<br><br>× \| 6 \| 12<br>90 \| 540 \| 1080<br>120 \| 720 \| 1440 |
| | 3 | a. 35 b. 91 c. 22 d. 35 |
| | 4 | a. First expression circled (20) b. First expression circled (3.5) c. First expression circled (791) |
| 15 | 1 | a. 7141 – 2634 b. 9025 – 7129 c. 2309 + 1699 |
| | 2 | 18,934 adults |
| | 3 | 521,224 |
| 17 | 1 | 417,488 |
| 18 | 2 | 63 |
| | 3 | a. £1457 b. £47.25 c. 6 flights d. 48 packs |
| | 4 | £228.33 |
| 20 | 1 | a. $\frac{2}{5}$ b. $\frac{7}{8}$ c. $\frac{5}{3}$ d. $2\frac{7}{10}$ e. $\frac{3}{4}$ f. $4\frac{3}{4}$ |
| | 2 | Different answers are possible for these questions. Use a calculator to check the answer.<br>Divide the numerator by the denominator to turn the fraction into a decimal. Do the same for the two given fractions and check to see whether your decimal lies between them.<br>a. Possible answers such as $\frac{17}{28}, \frac{18}{28}, \frac{19}{28}, \frac{20}{28}, \frac{10}{14}, \frac{5}{7}, \frac{9}{14}, \frac{6}{10}, \frac{3}{5}, \frac{7}{10}$ etc<br>b. Possible answers such as $\frac{11}{20}$<br>c. Possible answers such as $\frac{31}{48}$ |
| | 3 | $\frac{13}{24}, \frac{7}{12}, \frac{5}{8}, \frac{2}{3}, \frac{5}{6}$ |
| 22 | 1 | a. $\frac{1}{24}$ b. $6\frac{1}{24}$ e. $\frac{5}{8}$ |
| | 2 | $\frac{1}{48}$ |
| | 3 | 3180 children |
| | 4 | The explanation should include the fact that $\frac{3}{8}$ divided by 6 is equal to $\frac{3}{48}$ and, when this fraction is simplified is equal to $\frac{1}{16}$. |
| | 5 | $\frac{2}{9}$ and $5\frac{5}{9}$ |
| | 6 | a. $\frac{1}{36}$ b. $\frac{1}{18}$ |
| 24 | 1 | a. 86 b. 0.056 c. 50 d. 65 e. 3.677 f. 80.9 |
| | 2 | a. 2.4 b. 0.14 c. 27 |
| 25 | 3 | a. 6.617 b. 64.891 |
| | 4 | 0.6 |
| | 5 | 14 |
| | 6 | 0.006 |
| | 7 | 0.8 and 0.005 |

| Page | Q | Answers |
|---|---|---|
| 27 | 1 | a. 85% 0.85 b. 80% 0.8 |
| | 2 | a. 40% $\frac{2}{5}$ b. 37.5% $\frac{3}{8}$ |
| | 3 | 0.636 |
| | 4 | a. 0.7 b. 0.04 c. $\frac{5}{8}$ |
| | 5 | 0.9 litres, 90% |
| | 6 | 70% |
| 29 | 1 | a. 60% b. 55% c. 40% |
| | 2 | a. 70% b. 65% c. 76% d. 90% e. 92% f. 92% |
| 30 | 3 | a. 120 b. 105 c. 102 d. 8.4 |
| | 4 | £7.60 |
| | 5 | £33.15 |
| | 6 | 24mm |
| 32 | 1 | 8 free cups |
| | 2 | 12kg cement |
| | 3 | cement 254kg, sand 381kg |
| | 4 | 20:25 |
| | 5 | 1:2, 1:3 |
| | 6 | $y$ = 45.5cm |
| 34 | 1 | $C = 3 + 1.5 \times n$ or $C = 3 + 1.5n$ or $C = 1.5n + 3$ or $C = 1.5 \times n + 3$ |
| 35 | 2 | $C = 3 + 0.6 \times n$ or $C = 3 + 0.6n$ or $C = 0.6n + 3$ or $C = 0.6 \times n + 3$, £8.40 |
| | 3 | a. 11 b. 1 c. 11 d. 73 e. 36 f. 8 |
| | 4 | a. 8, 13, 18, 23 b. 7, 22, 43, 70 |
| | 5 | $2n + 1$ (or double the number then add 1; or add 3, then add 6, then add 12, doubling the amount you add each time) |
| | 6 | 6 56 10th term = 90 |
| 37 | 1 | a. 480 b. 4 c. 0.008 d. 240,000<br>e. 8000 f. 10 |
| | 2 | 0.05m |
| | 3 | 0.15m |
| | 4 | 36,000cm |
| | 5 | a. 40 miles b. 300 miles c. 75 miles |
| | 6 | a. 11.2km b. 19.2km c. 800km |
| 38 | 7 | An explanation that shows how 1km per second is equal to 60km per minute and 60 × 60 kilometres per hour which is 3600km/h. |
| | 8 | a. 16 b. 10 |
| | 9 | 300 |
| | 10 | 288 |
| 40 | 1 | a. 360g b. 95cm c. 5150m or 5.15km d. 0.4 litres e. 02:19<br>f. Sunday (16 July) |
| 41 | 2 | a = 17cm, b = 5cm, c = 6cm, d = 9cm, e = 13.5cm, f = 8cm, g = 7.5cm |
| | 3 | $x$ = 4cm, $y$ = 2.5cm |
| | 4 | $x$ = 7cm |
| 43 | 1 | a. area = 113cm$^2$, perimeter = 52cm b. area = 171cm$^2$, perimeter = 62cm<br>c. area = 196.25cm$^2$, perimeter = 62cm d. area = 85.75cm$^2$, perimeter = 56cm |

| Page | Q | Answers |
|---|---|---|
| 44 | 2 | $12cm^2$, 1.5cm |
| | 3 | Area of the trapezium = $\frac{1}{2}ah + hl + \frac{1}{2}bh$ or Area of the trapezium = $\frac{1}{2}(ah + bh) + hl$ or Area of the trapezium = $\frac{1}{2}h(a + b) + hl$ or Area of the trapezium = $h(\frac{1}{2}a + \frac{1}{2}b + l)$ or Area of the trapezium = $\frac{1}{2}h(a + b + 2l)$ . |
| | 4 | Area of the trapezium = $30 - \frac{1}{2}(5 \times 3.3) = 30 - \frac{1}{2}(16.5) = 30 - 8.25 = 21.75\ cm^2$ |
| 46 | 1 | a. $40cm^3$ b. $360m^3$ c. $300{,}000mm^3$ |
| | 2 | a. 4cm b. 10m c. 9mm |
| | 3 | a. There are many possible answers where the three numbers multiplied together make 150, such as: 10cm, 3cm, 5cm, or 25cm, 2cm, 3cm.<br>b. $27cm^3$<br>c. $686cm^3$ |
| 48 | 1 | a. kite or arrowhead b. right-angled isosceles triangle c. regular octagon<br>d. triangular prism e. cube or cuboid f. tetrahedron |
| 49 | 2 | 8 |
| | 3 | 25cm |
| | 4 | $r = \frac{1}{2}d$ |
| | 5 | a. tetrahedron b. triangular prism c. cuboid<br>d. pentagonal pyramid e. square pyramid f. hexagonal prism<br>Prisms are triangular prism, cuboid and hexagonal prism. |
| 51 | 1 | a. 58° b. 97° c. 139° d. 76° e. 135°, 45° and 135° f. 73° and 56° |
| | 2 | Obtuse angles: 97°, 113°, 139°, 112°, 135°, 107° |
| 52 | 3 | a = 120° (angles on a straight line = 180 so 180 − 60 = 120)<br>b = 70° (angles in a quadrilateral = 360° so 360 − (110 + 120 + 60) = 70)<br>c = 55° (if two lines cross, the opposite angles are equal)<br>d = 30° (angles in a triangle = 180° so 180 − 90 − 60 = 30)<br>e = 95° (opposite angles are equal so the third angle of the triangle equals 30°. The angles in a triangle = 180 so 180 − (55 + 30) = 95)<br>f = 65° (angles in a triangle = 180 so 180 − 65 − 50 = 65)<br>g. 115° (angles on a straight line = 180 so 180 − 65 = 115)<br>h. 115° (angles in a quadrilateral = 360° so 360 − (90 + 115 + 40) = 115) |
| 54 | 1 | a. horizontal b. vertical |

<table>
<tr><th>Page</th><th>Q</th><th>Answers</th></tr>
<tr><td rowspan="3">55</td><td>2</td><td>a. (4,−3) b. (2,1) c. (−1,4) d. (5,4)</td></tr>
<tr><td>3</td><td>a.<br>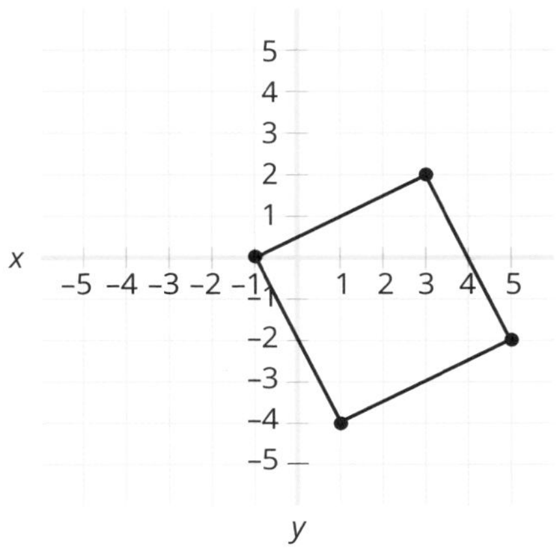
<br>b. (3,2)<br>c.<br>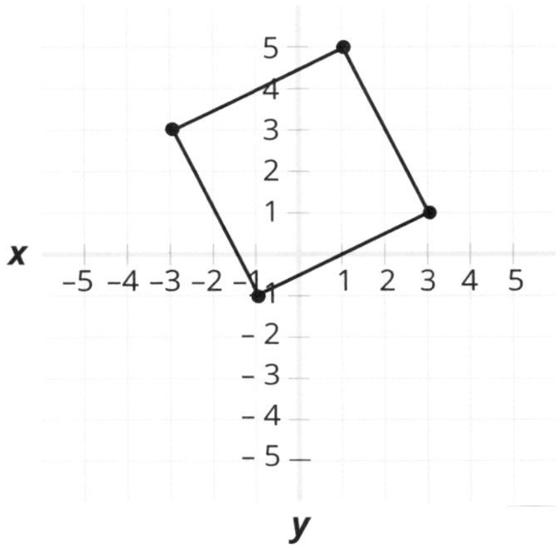
<br>d. (−3,3) (−1,−1) (3,1) (1,5)</td></tr>
<tr><td>4</td><td>a. (−2,−2) (−1,−1) (a,−b)<br>b. (2,2) (1,1) (−a,b)<br>c. (4,−2) (5,−3) (a + 6,b −4)</td></tr>
<tr><td>57</td><td>1</td><td>a. 6 b. 3.5 c. 2.2</td></tr>
<tr><td rowspan="3">58</td><td>2</td><td>a. 23 b. 15 c. 23 d. 25.1</td></tr>
<tr><td>3</td><td>a. 5° b. 120° c. 24 matches d. 30 matches</td></tr>
<tr><td>4</td><td><table>
<tr><th>Candidate</th><th>Angle of segment</th><th>Number of votes</th></tr>
<tr><td>Mr R. Brown</td><td>110</td><td>55</td></tr>
<tr><td>Ms J. Patel</td><td>140</td><td>70</td></tr>
<tr><td>Mrs L. Nagy</td><td>44</td><td>22</td></tr>
<tr><td>Ms J. Connors</td><td>44</td><td>22</td></tr>
<tr><td>Mr F. Fox</td><td>22</td><td>11</td></tr>
</table></td></tr>
</table>